2

5

9

6

An Illustrated Memoir

Ernst Stuhlinger

Frederick I. Ordway III

KRIEGER PUBLISHING COMPANY

Malabar, Florida
1994

Original Edition 1994

Printed and Published by
KRIEGER PUBLISHING COMPANY
KRIEGER DRIVE
MALABAR, FLORIDA 32950

Copyright © 1994 by Ernst Stuhlinger and Frederick I. Ordway III

Library of Congress Cataloging-In-Publication Data
Stuhlinger, Ernst, 1913-
    Wernher von Braun, crusader for space: an illustrated memoir / Ernst Stuhlinger and Frederick I. Ordway III.
       p.   cm.
    Issued simultaneously with Wernher von Braun, crusader for space: a biographical memoir.
    Includes index.
    ISBN 0-89464-824-1 (alk. paper)
    1. Von Braun, Wernher, 1912-1977. 2. Rocketry — Biography.
I. Ordway, Frederick Ira, 1927-   . II. Title.
TL781.85.V6S783   1994
621.43' 56' 092 — dc20
[B]   93-10678
                                               CIP

10   9   8   7   6   5   4   3   2

To all

who believe in mankind's future

in space

Contents

Captions for Front and Back Montage

1. Von Braun at the podium during ceremonies on 24 February 1970 in downtown Huntsville shortly before his departure for NASA headquarters in Washington, D.C. Between him and his wife Maria stands Harry M. Rhett, Jr., leading businessman and banker.

2. A group of NASA officials observes the 25 May 1965 launch of the Saturn I SA-8 vehicle from Complex 37 at Cape Canaveral, Florida. Pointing at center is Dr. Kurt H. Debus, Kennedy Space Center director. To the right is Dr. Hans Gruene of Kennedy; Dr. Wernher von Braun, director of NASA-Marshall; and (leaning) Dr. Eberhard F. M. Rees. Directly above von Braun is Bob Moser, Kennedy launch director; and above Rees (standing) is Albert Zeiler.

3. Wernher von Braun and Maria von Quistorp marry at Landshut, Bavaria on 1 March 1947. Left to right Albrecht von Quistorp, Maria's brother; Sigismund von Braun, Wernher's brother; Wilhelm Edzard, Prince of Innhausen and Knyphausen, Maria's uncle; Theda von Quistorp, Maria's mother; and Emmy and Magnus von Braun, Wernher's parents. *Illustrierte Bunte*/ Burda GmbH, Germany/Von Braun Archives.

4. Dr. von Braun and his family gather at the Smithsonian Institution in Washington, D.C., on the occasion of his being awarded the Langley Medal on 4 June 1967. Young Peter holds the distinguished award for his father.

5. Formal photo-portrait of von Braun taken in celebration of his 50th birthday, March 1962. Courtesy Fabian Bachrach/Von Braun Archives.

6. Von Braun at 24 years old, in his Luftwaffe cadet uniform.

7. Maria and Wernher von Braun vacationing in Hawaii, 1959. Courtesy Hawaiian Airlines/ Von Braun Archives.

8. Von Braun holds son Peter Constantine, who was born on 2 June 1960 in Huntsville, Alabama.

9. The von Braun children as they appeared in 1960. Left to right: Iris Careen, born 1948; Margrit Cecile, born 1952; and Peter Constantine, born 1960.

10. Arthur Fiedler, conductor of the Boston Pops Orchestra, von Braun, and Mrs. Fiedler meet in von Braun's office on 23 March 1962.

11. Walt Disney, left, and von Braun, right, during production of the "Tomorrowland" television series on spaceflight, 1954.

12. In mid-November 1967, von Braun prepares for a dive at Marshall's neutral buoyancy tank.

13. President John F. Kennedy discusses the planned Apollo missions to the Moon with von Braun during a tour of the NASA-Marshall Space Flight Center on 11 September 1962.

14. Dr. Martin Schilling, left; Stuhlinger, center; and von Braun, right, sign their U.S. citizenship papers in April 1955.

15. Rudolf Nebel, left, and 18-year-old Wernher von Braun carry Mirak rockets at the flight test field Raketenflugplatz in Berlin-Reinickendorf, 1930.

16. Von Braun relaxes moments after the Saturn V launch vehicle has lofted Apollo 11 and its three-man crew towards the Moon on 16 July 1969, Cape Canaveral, Florida.

17. Colonel Miles Chatfield, chief, Ordnance Guided Missile Laboratories; Army Ballistic Missile Agency commander Major General John B. Medaris; von Braun; Brigadier General Holger Toftoy, commander of Redstone Arsenal; and Colonel John R. Nickerson shortly after the creation of the new agency on 1 February 1956.

18. President Dwight D. Eisenhower confers the President's Award for Distinguished Federal Civilian Service on von Braun, 20 January 1959, accompanied by Secretary of the Army Wilbur Brucker.

FOREWORD

I was one of the lucky ones, having worked with Dr. Wernher von Braun in the 1960s at NASA's George C. Marshall Space Flight Center in Huntsville, Alabama.

At the time, I was an eager public relations specialist hanging onto his every word. Eventually, we became friends and then allies in the dream to build a space science education program and a world-class center to incorporate it. He believed there should be a place where citizens of the United States and other nations could share in the rapidly growing space experience. The result is the U.S. Space & Rocket Center, which opened close to von Braun's Marshall Center in 1970 — nearly a quarter of a century ago.

It was on Space & Rocket Center grounds where his observation of visiting school children scribbling notes inspired the idea for what became U.S. Space Camp and later U.S. Space Academy and Aviation Challenge. Von Braun looked upon today's children as tomorrow's explorers, the ones who would keep the dream alive of expeditions to the Moon, to Mars and other beckoning worlds of the Solar System.

He often said that we should not think in terms of building for today; rather, we should constantly seek to invest in the future. He would be proud to know that since 1982 hundreds of thousands of young students have graduated from Space Camp, Space Academy and Aviation Challenge with renewed enthusiasm for science, engineering, mathematics, aeronautics, and astronautics.

Today, I still marvel at his vision and sense of purpose. He didn't wonder if we could put a man in space or set foot on the Moon; he *knew* it could be done. And, better yet, he understood just how to do it.

The myriad photographs and drawings in this illustrated memoir *Wernher von Braun: Crusader for Space* will rekindle fond memories for those who were close to the man. The book is an insightful historical study for all who remember his accomplishments and contributions — and an inspiration for those too young to have known him. Wernher von Braun helped us touch the Moon and planets and left behind a blueprint for exploring the universe at large. I miss him as must all seekers of tomorrow.

Edward O. Buckbee, Director
U.S. Space & Rocket Center

PREFACE

Some three decades ago, we collaborated with Jerry C. McCall and George C. Bucher to celebrate von Braun's fiftieth birthday with a volume entitled *From Peenemünde to Outer Space*.[1] Within its 853 pages were forty papers dedicated to a respected master. All were written by scientists and engineers who had enjoyed the privilege of working with him at Peenemünde, Germany; Fort Bliss, Texas, and White Sands, New Mexico; Cape Canaveral, Florida; and Huntsville, Alabama. From this large original NASA-released volume a shorter book of nearly 400 pages was published commercially. Containing eighteen papers, a prologue and an epilogue, it appeared under the title *Astronautical Engineering and Science: From Peenemünde to Planetary Space*.[2]

We ended our preface with these words: "Your first 50 years have been filled with magnificent accomplishments, yet they are only a prelude to what the future may bring: for you, the fulfillment of your boldest dream, a trip to the planet Mars — and for the rest of us, your safe return to Earth."

Now, more than three decades later, somewhat past von Braun's eightieth birthday, and with manned missions to Mars still reserved for the future, we present this biographical memoir of one of the twentieth century's more remarkable figures. In planning the work with the publisher, we jointly decided that our purpose in researching and writing the life of Wernher von Braun could best be served by the appearance of two volumes. The first would be descriptive and interpretative — the prose memoir, while the second would focus on the visual image — the illustrated memoir. From our and other archives we present a gallery of photographs, many never before published, that we hope will supplement the written account to provide a more complete picture of the subject of our labors for more than a decade.

While the central theme in von Braun's life was the development of rockets and space-craft, our book does not dwell on the many technical details implicit in their description. Other books have already done this for us. Rather, we intend to answer the simple question: What kind of man was Wernher von Braun? Our book is the first — and probably will be the last — biographical memoir written by authors who have been closely and personally associated with the man during a substantial part of his life, Ordway for twenty-five and Stuhlinger for thirty-four years.

Ernst Stuhlinger
Frederick I. Ordway III

---

[1] Stuhlinger, Ernst, Frederick I. Ordway III, Jerry C. McCall and George C. Bucher, editors, *From Peenemünde to Outer Space*. Huntsville, Alabama, 1962: NASA-George C. Marshall Space Flight Center.

[2] Stuhlinger, Ernst, Frederick I. Ordway III, Jerry C. McCall and George C. Bucher, editors, *Astronautical Engineering and Science: From Peenemünde to Planetary Space*. New York, 1963: McGraw-Hill Book Company.

ACKNOWLEDGMENTS

Unless otherwise noted, the photographs reproduced in this volume are from the Stuhlinger and Ordway archives and those of the late Wernher von Braun, which are located at the U.S. Space & Rocket Center in Huntsville, Alabama.

The authors are grateful for the help of Edward O. Buckbee, Scott Osborne, James Hagler, and Doris Hunter, U.S. Space & Rocket Center; Chieko Inman, Annette K. Tingle, and Michael D. Wright, NASA-Marshall Space Flight Center; Dr. Roger D. Launius and Lee Saegesser, NASA Headquarters History Office; Jacqueline L. Foster, Gwen Pitman and Althea Washington, NASA Headquarters Media Services/Audio Visual; Mark Herring, NASA-Stennis Space Center; Dr. Richard Tousey, U.S. Naval Research Laboratory; Lori Garver and David Brandt, National Space Society; and Irvin Singer and J. B. Minnich, Fairchild Industries.

Also, Dr. Carsbie C. Adams, hospital administrator; Brigadier General Julius Braun, U.S. Army (ret.); Dr. Konrad K. Dannenberg, NASA-Marshall (ret.); Frederick C. Durant III, former president of the American Rocket Society and International Astronautical Federation; Dr. Robert C. Gilruth, NASA-Johnson (ret.); Charles C. Hewitt, former executive director, National Space Institute; Karl Heimburg, NASA-Marshall (ret.); Dr. I. M. Levitt, former director of the Fels Planetarium, Franklin Institute; Ron Miller, space artist; Erich and Margot Neubert, NASA-Marshall (ret.); Rudolf and Dorette Schlidt, NASA-Marshall (ret.); Mitchell R. Sharpe, NASA-Marshall (ret.) and consultant, U.S. Space & Rocket Center; A. F. Staats, former president of the Hermann Oberth Society; Maria von Braun; and Major General John Zierdt, U.S. Army (ret.).

BIOGRAPHICAL SKETCH

When *Life* magazine published "The Life 100 Most Important Americans of the 20th Century,"[1] it characterized Wernher von Braun as the man who "launched the greatest adventure of all — to the Moon." A similar evaluation was advanced in the journal *Ad Astra's* "100 Stars of Space":[2] "No other person has had as much impact in bringing the space program to where it is today." And in the aerospace trade magazine *Aviation Week and Space Technology,*[3] the editors wondered — on the occasion of the twentieth anniversary of mankind's first landing on the Moon — "Where are the U.S. space visionaries of comparable stature today?"

Wernher Magnus Maximilian von Braun was born to Baron Magnus von Braun and Emmy von Quistorp on 23 March 1912 in Wirsitz, a town in the eastern German province of Posen. The elder von Braun was a provincial councillor, one of the founders of the Deutsche Rentenbank savings institution, and served as Minister for Agriculture during the early 1930s in President Paul von Hindenburg's short-lived Weimar Republic. Baroness von Braun came from a distinguished Swedish-German family.

From childhood, young Wernher revealed an interest in both science and music. At the age of eleven he enrolled in the Französisches Gymnasium that had been established two centuries earlier by Frederick the Great. There, the lad exhibited but modest ability in mathematics and physics, subjects in which he would later excel. In 1928, Wernher's father placed him in the progressive Hermann Lietz schools, first at Ettersburg and subsequently on Spiekeroog Island. Wernher's grades and scholastic attitude improved at both.

The next step for the now eighteen-year-old Wernher von Braun was to enter the Technische Hochschule in the Berlin district of Charlottenburg and at the same time to become an apprentice at the locomotive manufacturer Borsigwerke. All the while, his interest in astronomy and space travel kept growing. He had become acquainted with astronautics pioneer Hermann Oberth, writer and spaceflight popularizer Willy Ley, and rocket experimenters Rudolf Nebel and Johannes Winkler. He had also followed with great interest the exploits of Max Valier who had gained considerable publicity driving automobiles and rail cars propelled by rockets. This exposure soon led von Braun to join the Verein für Raumshiffahrt (VfR, Society for Space Travel) and to participate in its rocket experiments at the Raketenflugplatz located on a vacant Army proving ground near Reinickendorf.

To broaden his academic background, von Braun spent a semester at the Eidgenössische Technische Hochschule in Zurich, Switzerland, before returning to Germany to complete requirements for his aeronautical engineering degree at Charlottenburg.

Events accelerated from then on. On 1 November 1932, von Braun signed a contract with the Reichswehr (Army Ordnance) to conduct research leading to the development of rockets as military weapons. In this capacity, he worked for the man who would be his boss for over a decade, Captain (later, Major General) Walter Dornberger. In the same year, under an army grant, von Braun enrolled at the Friedrich-Wilhelm-Universität from where he graduated two years later with a Ph.D. in physics. His dissertation dealt with theoretical and practical problems of liquid propellant rocket engines.

Even before he had completed his studies and could devote full time at the Army's Kummersdorf artillery range outside Berlin, von Braun began the work that would occupy him for the rest of his career and bring him worldwide recognition and honors.

His initial endeavor was to refine a primitive VfR rocket, but results were disappointing: it exploded within seconds of ignition on the night of 21 December 1932. Being an engineer himself, Dornberger was not unduly perturbed for he realized that invaluable lessons could be gleaned from even unsuccessful test firings. Meanwhile, the nucleus of what would become the von Braun "rocket team" solidified as several colleagues from the VfR days began working at Kummersdorf.

The appropriately designated A-1 was the first rocket to be developed at Kummersdorf. Weighing 150 kilograms, it burned liquid oxygen and ethyl alcohol and produced 300 kilograms of thrust. By 1934, it evolved into the more stable A-2, two of which were launched in December from Borkum Island in the North Sea. These tests successfully demonstrated that fairly sizable rockets could be controlled gyroscopically.

By 1935, von Braun and his team, which had grown to eighty members, were regularly static-firing engines with thrusts as high as 1,000 to 1,500 kilograms. All the while, Dornberger was concerned that they would soon outgrow the Kummersdorf facility if still larger rockets then on the drawing boards were developed and tested. The need to find a secure, isolated location was apparent.

As it turned out, it was von Braun's mother who suggested such a site on the Baltic Sea at the mouth of the river Peene on the island of Usedom — Peenemünde. Since the German Luftwaffe was working closely with Army Ordnance at the time on the development and flight testing of rocket-powered airplanes, it seemed reasonable that the two branches of military service should collaborate in the purchase and development of the site.

This approach was followed, and the two services soon entered into negotiations to construct a complex that called for an experimental airfield and supporting structures for the Luftwaffe together with an array of installations required for designing, developing, manufacturing and firing a variety of rockets and ballistic missiles for Army Ordnance. The services purchased the site from the town of Wolgast for Reichsmarks 750,000.

During the construction of the Peenemünde complex, rocket development continued at Kummersdorf. In March 1939, Hitler decided to drop in for briefings and test firings. Though he didn't appear overly impressed with what he heard and saw, the Führer made no effort to interfere with activities there.

Some 140 kilometers to the north of Kummersdorf what became known officially as Heeresversuchsstelle Peenemünde (Army Research Center, Peenemünde) was coming to life. As soon as the site was ready, efforts began to develop more advanced rockets including the A-4. Designed to carry a one-metric-ton warhead, this ballistic missile was to reach targets more than 300 kilometers distant. In a few short years, the A-4 would become known as the infamous V-2 vengeance weapon.

As work progressed on the A-4 and other rockets — including the Wasserfall antiaircraft weapon — the Donberger-von Braun team had grown to nearly 2,000 scientists and engineers and close to 4,000 other personnel. By 1942, the annual payroll had reached RM 13 million (nearly U.S. $3 million). After several tries, an A-4 was successfully launched for the first time on 3 October of that year ushering in the age of the long-range precision rocket. Still, much work remained: a single success did not translate into a proven weapon system; it would be another two years before the missile would be deployed in the field.

Less than a year after the first A-4 success, the British became suspicious of goings on at Peenemünde. In mid-August 1943, hundreds of Royal Air Force Lancaster bombers attacked the site causing rather extensive damage. The raid led to the decision by the Germans to disperse many of Peenemünde's activities including A-4 missile production. Von Braun, however, remained there until near the end of the war.

A major scare occurred in mid-March 1944 when von Braun was arrested by the Gestapo and imprisoned in Stettin. The alleged crime: declaring that his main interest in developing the A-4 was its potential for space travel rather than as a weapon that would turn the tide of war in Germany's favor. Also, since he regularly piloted his government-provided airplane, it was suggested he might be planning to escape with A-4 secrets to the Allies. Only through the personal intervention of Munitions and Armaments Minister Albert Speer with Hitler would von Braun be released from jail and allowed to return to his duties.

In 1943, Reichsführer SS Heinrich Himmler forced component manufacturing, missile assembly, and military deployment of the A-4 out of the hands of Dornberger and von Braun who wanted to continue improving and testing the still immature rocket before releasing it for production. The underground factory Mittelwerk, established in 1943, began producing A-4s late that year along with other weapons. Several thousand inmates from nearby concentration camps, together with about as many civilian workers, worked at the plant. Beginning in September 1944, A-4s — now called V-2s — were launched against Paris, London, Antwerp, and other targets.

By early 1945, von Braun realized that Peenemünde might soon be overrun by Soviet troops from the east. In mid-February, the final V-2 launch took place from Peenemünde and a week later von Braun and many of his teammates departed for the south.

Moving into Thuringia, he attempted to regroup but to no avail; the situation was becoming chaotic, with the Americans and British closing in from the west and the Russians from the east. The rocket team scattered throughout Germany during March and April; von Braun, his brother Magnus, Dornberger and others ended up in a resort lodge in Oberjoch near the Austrian border. In early May, they all surrendered to units of the American 44th Infantry Division and were immediately taken to the Austrian town of Reutte for preliminary interrogations. Later, the group was transferred back to Bavaria.

During the summer, interrogation by the Allies continued. The Americans soon offered von Braun and some 120 key members of his team a six-month contract to work for Army Ordnance in the United States. The offer was accepted. Von Braun and six teammates made up the first contingent to leave Europe; on 20 September they arrived at Fort Strong in Boston Harbor. From there, von Braun continued to Washington, D.C. for briefings. Finally, he left by train for Fort Bliss near El Paso, Texas, where, during the following months, he was joined by the rest of his team. A new chapter in the history of rocketry was about to be written.

At the newly established White Sands Proving Ground in New Mexico some 80 miles north of Fort Bliss, the von Braun team helped to assemble and check out V-2s brought over from Germany, to train American soldiers in the art and science of rocketry, and to advise representatives of industrial firms interested in becoming active in the rocket and missile field. During the team's five years at Fort Bliss and White Sands, dozens of V-2s carrying instruments designed to study the upper atmosphere, solar radiations, and the frontier of space were successfully launched. The team's original six-month temporary contract soon became permanent employment.

Von Braun left for the Bavarian town of Landshut towards the end of winter 1947 to marry his cousin Maria von Quistorp. Soon after the wedding, which took place on 1 March, the couple traveled to the States accompanied by von Braun's father and mother who wished to be with their sons Wernher and Magnus in Texas. In December 1948, Maria gave birth to daughter Iris. She was followed four years later by Margrit and in 1960 by Peter.

During the Fort Bliss-White Sands years, von Braun began writing his first book: *Das Marsprojekt*, or *The Mars Project*. It dealt with a voyage to Mars in the not-too-distant future by a fleet of spaceships powered by advanced liquid propellant rocket engines. The book first appeared in Germany in 1952 and, in English translation, the following year in the United States. Von Braun, looking for more exciting projects than launching converted wartime missiles from the New Mexico desert, dreamed of the future in the pages of his manuscript.

The Army estimated that the practice of sending American scientists and engineers to confer and work with the Germans during the Fort Bliss-White Sands years gained ten years in directing U.S. research and development into channels that would ultimately prove successful. As for the monetary value of the accumulated know-how, equipment and documentation, a figure of at least $750 million seems reasonable.

The von Braun rocket team had entered the United States without valid passports and visas; Army Ordnance referred to its German wards as "prisoners of peace." If the men were ultimately to remain permanently in the country, arrangements would have to be made for their legal entry. So when von Braun and his teammates were offered permanent employment, they were taken from El Paso to nearby Juarez in Mexico where the American consulate issued them visas. The men then legally reentered the United States — by streetcar!

At the close of the 1940s, Army Ordnance realized that facilities at Fort Bliss would be inadequate to support a major advance in missile technology, much less the development of vehicles capable of flying into space. So the search began for a suitable alternative site. Now it so happened that two adjacent arsenals in Huntsville, Alabama, had been deactivated after World War II and were for sale. Following a visit by von Braun, Colonel Holger N. Toftoy, and Major James P. Hamill in September 1949, the decision was made to transfer there the 100 plus Germans and about 300 other personnel from Fort Bliss and White Sands. The two arsenals were quickly consolidated into the Redstone Arsenal; and, beginning in April 1950, men and equipment from Texas were installed in Alabama.

From 1950 to 1970, von Braun lived, worked, and promoted space travel in the rapidly growing town of Huntsville. When he first arrived, signs proclaimed it to be the "Watercress Capital of the World." A few years later new signs read "Rocket Capital of the World" and still later "Space Capital U.S.A."

A couple of years after settling into his missile development work at Redstone Arsenal, von Braun began seriously to campaign for space. He lectured whenever the opportunity arose. With several colleagues, he wrote popular articles on space travel for *Collier's* and other magazines and worked with Walt Disney on several television productions depicting space stations and voyages to the Moon and Mars.

More professionally, in mid-September 1954, von Braun submitted a report to his military commander at Redstone, Colonel Holger N. Toftoy, with the somewhat daunting title "A Minimum Satellite Vehicle Based on Components Available from Missile Developments of the Army Ordnance Corps." It called for launching a small satellite by a multistage rocket consisting of a Redstone booster plus solid-propellant upper stages. This report formed the basis for a joint Army-Navy satellite proposal designated Project Orbiter. Unfortunately for von Braun and his colleagues, the Orbiter plans were not accepted; the U.S. Government opted instead for an all-Navy launch vehicle-satellite configuration known as Vanguard to be flown during the 1957-58 International Geophysical Year.

American citizenship was granted Wernher von Braun, his brother Magnus, some forty other team members, and their respective wives in mid-April 1955, ten years after most of them had arrived in the United States. Meanwhile, the team had already commenced developing a large, liquid-propellant, intermediate-range ballistic missile (later named Jupiter) capable of carrying a nuclear payload to a distance of 1,600 miles. To von Braun this was an important milestone in his career for he was now working on a rocket capable of launching heavier satellites than envisioned for Project Orbiter and one that could even send a small spacecraft towards the Moon.

The Army Ballistic Missile Agency (ABMA) was created at Redstone Arsenal on 1 February 1956 with the mission of developing and fielding the Jupiter IRBM. Von Braun's new boss, ABMA commander Brigadier General John B. Medaris (later Major General), was given broad authority to move the project towards rapid completion. The team grew rapidly, augmented by "second generation" Germans recruited to work with the charismatic von Braun. The highlight of 1956 came on 20 September when a Redstone-based Jupiter-C (for composite) rocket with two solid-rocket upper stages (much like those proposed in Project Orbiter) reached an altitude of 682 miles and a range of 3,400 miles. (The "Jupiter" designation for a Redstone-based configuration allowed the multistage rocket to enjoy the Jupiter IRBM's high national priority.)

On May 31 of the following year, von Braun witnessed the first launching of the Jupiter IRBM from Cape Canaveral. Then, on 8 August, another Jupiter-C was sent into the lower fringes of space to test a scale model of the nose cone that would insulate the atomic warhead of the Jupiter IRBM as it reentered the Earth's atmosphere. Things were beginning to look up for von Braun and his team at ABMA for they were proving their ability to build rockets capable of sending payloads into space.

The startling news that Sputnik 1 had been orbited by the Soviet Union on 4 October 1957, coupled with the unhappy inauguration of the American Vanguard project, convinced the U.S. Government to authorize Medaris and von Braun to prepare an Army attempt to enter what had become the space race. Working with Dr. William H. Pickering's team at the Army-owned Jet Propulsion Laboratory in California, and Dr. James A. Van Allen's team at the state University of Iowa, by late January a Juno I rocket (a Jupiter-C with a solid-propellant-powered fourth stage added) and its small satellite payload were ready.

Temporarily delayed because of high winds above Cape Canaveral, the Juno I finally lifted off its launch pad shortly before 11 PM on 31 January 1958. Von Braun, who had been ordered to be in Washington, waited nervously in a room deep in the Pentagon with an equally nervous Pickering and others involved in the mission. Word reached them that the Juno I rocket had functioned well. But, nothing about the satellite. Had something gone wrong? After a seeming eternity, signals from Explorer 1 — the name given America's first successful satellite — were picked up in California and a little later in Florida. The Medaris-von Braun Army team had triumphed: the Soviet Union was no longer the only spacefaring nation. Other Juno I-orbited satellites followed as well as spacecraft launched by the larger Juno II (a Jupiter IRBM plus Juno I upper stages).

For some time, von Braun and his colleagues had been studying launch vehicle configurations of far greater lifting capabilities than Redstone and Jupiter-based carriers. He was therefore delighted when, in mid-August 1958, authorization reached him to begin work on a huge booster developing 1.5 million pounds of thrust. To minimize cost, he decided to cluster available propellant tanks, pumps, and rocket engines. In other words, already flight-tested Redstone and Jupiter components would become the booster's building blocks. It was baptized Saturn, the next planet in the solar system out from Jupiter.

Von Braun's enthusiasm for the booster assignment was tempered by uncertainties as to whether his Development Operations Division at ABMA was about to be taken away from the Army and incorporated into the new National Aeronautics and Space Administration (NASA).

While von Braun pondered his future, on 20 January 1959 President Eisenhower bestowed on him the President's Award for Distinguished Federal Civilian Service, the highest honor given to a civilian employee of the United States Government. Despite the honor, von Braun's and ABMA's morale suffered as the year wore on; continuation of Saturn funding had become uncertain for the simple reason that the Army did not have an approved mission for such a large rocket at a time when most space projects were being handed over to NASA.

Rumors that von Braun's Development Operations Division would be transferred from ABMA to NASA were confirmed in mid-January 1960. The mass transfer of personnel and facilities soon followed and on 1 July the George C. Marshall Space

Flight Center officially came into being under von Braun's directorship. Marshall's primary responsibility was to be launch vehicles, including Saturn, and their propulsion systems.

Still, there was no officially sanctioned mission for the Saturn. That is, not until May 1961 when newly elected President Kennedy announced a national goal to reach the Moon by the end of the decade. Von Braun's dreams suddenly appeared realistic as the United States geared up for an astonishing new endeavor. "Now is the time to take longer strides" the president had said, "time for a greater new America, time for this nation to take a clearly leading role in space achievement which in many ways may hold the key to our future on Earth . . . I believe," he continued, "that this nation should commit itself to achieving the goal of landing a man on the Moon and returning him safely to Earth."

Throughout the 1960s, von Braun and his team worked night and day as they designed, developed, built, and tested what became the Saturn family of launch vehicles: Saturn I, Saturn IB, and Saturn V. On 9 November 1967, an event took place that he would rank in personal excitement and importance with the launching of the first successful A-4 (V-2) back in October 1942 and the orbiting of Explorer 1 in late January 1958. The very first Saturn V soared from its Kennedy Space Center launch pad in a nearly flawless maiden flight.

Other Saturn Vs followed, sending Apollo spacecraft around the Moon in late 1968 and the spring of 1969; and, beginning with Apollo 11 on 16 July of the same year, onto the lunar surface. When the expeditions to the Moon came to an end with Apollo 17 in December 1972, the von Braun team at Marshall turned its efforts to Skylab, the first U.S. space station. But von Braun himself was no longer with his teammates, for in 1970 he had moved from Huntsville to Washington to become NASA's deputy associate administrator in charge of advanced planning. Two years later, aware that America was no longer prone to support large-scale — and costly — space endeavors, von Braun resigned to take up the position of vice president for engineering and development at Fairchild Industries located in nearby Germantown, Maryland.

At Fairchild, he became a strong supporter of the Applications Technology Satellite 6 program for which Fairchild was the prime NASA contractor. ATS-6 proved to be an excellent example of how space technology could be dedicated to improving the lot of humanity on Earth. Shortly after its launch in May 1974, von Braun began lecturing to leaders in Europe, Asia and South America how advances in satellite technology, as demonstrated by ATS-6, could provide communications, educational and other practical services.

All the while, he was devoting considerable time and energy to the organization and growth of the National Space Institute, a pro-space membership society supported in part by corporate grants.

Due to failing health, at the end of December 1976 von Braun retired from Fairchild and gave up his duties at the National Space Institute. In January, President Ford awarded him the National Medal of Science. Death came to Wernher von Braun in Alexandria, Virginia, on 16 June 1977. Six days later, a special memorial service was held for him at Washington's National Cathedral. There, many friends and colleagues spoke of his remarkable character and lifetime achievements. In a statement issued following von Braun's death, President Carter called him " . . . a man of bold vision . . . Not just the people of our nation, but all the people of the world have profited from his work. We will continue to profit from his example."

That was more than seventeen years ago. How are von Braun's life and contributions assessed today? Author Mike Gray, writing in his 1992 book *Angle of Attack*,[4] found von Braun to be "...unique to the twentieth century. Like Columbus before him, he was shaped by the accident of being precisely the right man for the job at the moment the tools were invented... Von Braun was at least his (Columbus') equal." Another author, William J. Walter, wrote in his Space Age[5] that "It was difficult to imagine a person more perfectly fashioned for the Space Age than Wernher von Braun . . . His ambition was enormous and unrelenting, yet it rarely seemed petty or self-serving. It is difficult to imagine how the Space Age would have unfolded in this century without von Braun. When he died it symbolized the passing of an era."

---

[1] "The Life 100 Most Important Americans of the 20th Century," *Life*, Fall 1990, Vol 13 No. 12, p. 50.

[2] "Wernher von Braun," *Ad Astra*, July/August 1991 Vol. 3 No. 6, pp. 16-17.

[3] "The Legacy of Apollo 11" (editorial), *Aviation Week and Space Technology*, 17 July 1989, p. 7.

[4] Gray, Mike, *Angle of Attack: Harrison Storms and the Race to the Moon.* New York, 1992: W. W. Norton & Company, p. 44.

[5] Walter, William J., *Space Age.* New York, 1992: Random House, p. 97. (This book is the companion volume to the National Academy of Sciences/Public Broadcasting System six-part television series of the same name; it was broadcast nationwide in the autumn of 1992.)

I

*Childhood, Youth
and Academic Development
in Germany*

1912-1932

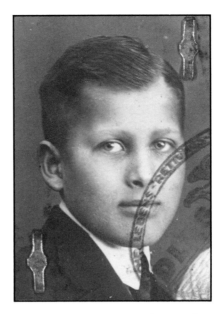

Ten-year-old Wernher von Braun pictured in a white suit standing among his schoolmates at the French Gymnasium (Französisches Gymnasium) in Berlin. Young Wernher did poorly at this school, which had been created some 200 years earlier by Frederick the Great of Prussia for children of French Huguenots who had been persecuted by Louis XIV.

Fourteen-year-old Wernher photographed for his life-saving certificate. Von Braun exhibited interest in many areas — life saving being only one — in which he tried to excel.

Magnus and Emmy von Braun's three children photographed together at their Berlin residence in 1924. Left to right: Wernher, 12; Sigismund, 13; and Magnus, 5.

The photographer clearly did not attempt to elicit smiles from these three serious young lads.

Wernher von Braun, fourth from left with hat and now 15 years old, sits next to his teacher at the Hermann Lietz School at Ettersburg Castle near Weimar. There, he dedicated himself more fully to his studies, pleasing his parents as his grades improved markedly.

In the early 1920s, when von Braun was living in Berlin, he studied piano under the famous German composer Paul Hindemith (1895-1963). By the time he was 15, Wernher had begun composing, including what he cited as "Three Short Pieces for Piano."

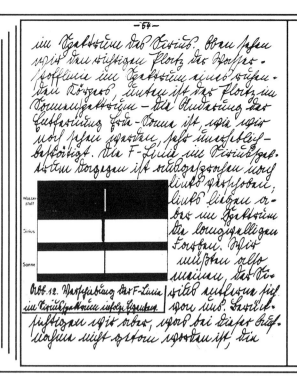

A year later, in 1928, the then 16-year-old Wernher tried his hand at writing. These extracts are from his manuscript "Aus der Geschichte der Astronomie" ("Glimpses at the History of Astronomy"). He wonders: "Shouldn't even the most primitive aborigines . . . have raised their yearning eyes toward the stars that every night adorned the celestial dome above their heads?"

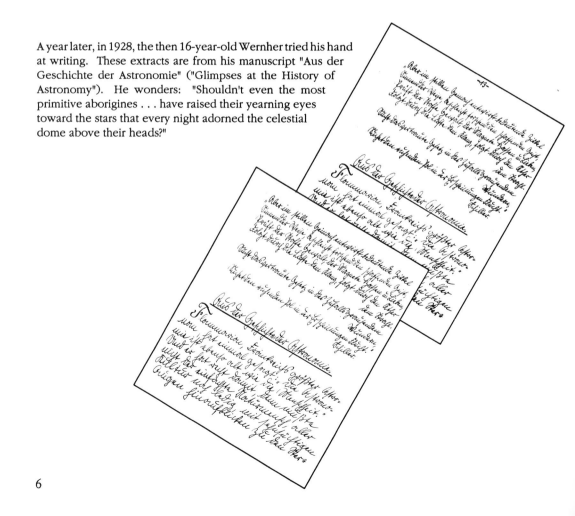

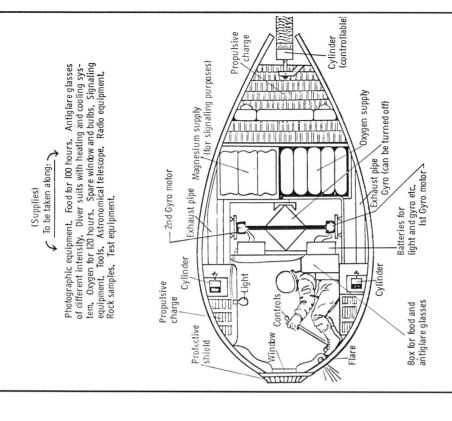

Propulsive charge

Cylinder (controllable)

Magnesium supply (for signaling purposes)

Oxygen supply

2nd Gyro motor

Exhaust pipe

Exhaust pipe

Gyro (can be turned off)

1st Gyro motor

Batteries for light and gyro etc.

Propulsive charge

Cylinder

Light

Protective shield

Window

Controls

Flare

Box for food and antiglare glasses

Cylinder

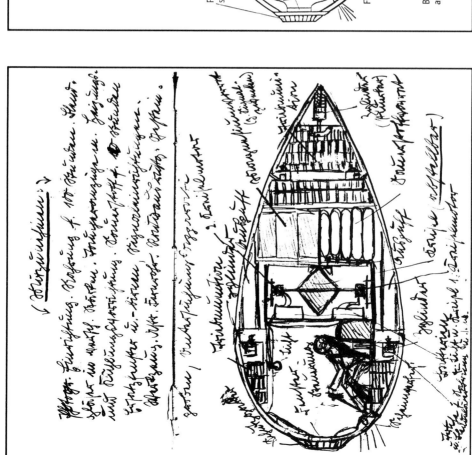

Young Wernher composed music, wrote on astronomy, and also learned how to sketch as demonstrated by this 1928 rendition of an orbiting spacecraft. A translation into English appears at the right.

Photo-portrait of
Wernher von Braun
at age 17.

Von Braun dressed in heavy overcoat and scarf, c. 1930

1.)

In einem Zylinderquer... soll die Dachfläche konzentrisch gegen die Boden-fläche um einen Winkel u gedreht werden. Die Länge einer Fragkante s ist als Funktion von u auszudrücken. Ferner ist der Winkel φ zu bestimmen und die Resultate für s und φ durch Entwickeln von u in eine Potenzreihe zu geben. Schließlich ist der eingeschlossene Winkel zweier Fragkanten vom Abstand ε zu ermitteln und anzugeben für die Werte $h = 2r$, $u = \frac{\pi}{2}$, $\varepsilon = \frac{2}{3}r$.

$$\frac{b/2}{r} = \sin\frac{u}{2} \quad ; \quad b = 2r\sin\frac{u}{2}$$
$$s^2 = h^2 + b^2 = h^2 + 4r^2\sin^2\frac{u}{2}$$
$$s = \pm\sqrt{h^2 + 4r^2\sin^2\frac{u}{2}}$$

2.)

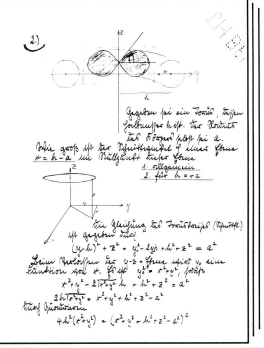

Gegeben sei ein Torus, dessen Halbmesser... der Kontur und Torus... plus a. Wie groß ist der Schnittwinkel φ einer Ebene $x = h - a$ mit Rückfläche dieses Torus

1. allgemein
2. für $h = +a$

Die Gleichung des Toruskreises (Schnitte) ist gegeben durch
$$(y-h)^2 + z^2 = y^2 - 2yh + h^2 + z^2 = a^2$$
Beim Verdrehen der y-z-Ebene wird y eine Funktion von x. Es ist $y^2 = x^2 + y^2$, so daß
$$x^2 + y^2 - 2\sqrt{x^2+y^2}\,h + h^2 + z^2 = a^2$$
$$2h\sqrt{x^2+y^2} = x^2+y^2+h^2+z^2-a^2$$
Durch Quadrieren
$$4h^2(x^2+y^2) = (x^2+y^2+h^2+z^2-a^2)^2$$

Untersuche die folgenden alternierenden Reihen auf ihre Konvergenz.

1.) $\quad 1 - \frac{1}{2} + \frac{1}{3} - \frac{1}{4}\cdots$

$\left[1 - \frac{1}{2}\right] + \left[\frac{1}{3} - \frac{1}{4}\right] + \left[\frac{1}{5} - \frac{1}{6}\right]\cdots$

$+\frac{1}{2} + \frac{1}{12} + \frac{1}{30} + \frac{1}{56}\cdots$

$+\frac{1}{3} - \frac{1}{4} = \frac{1}{12}$

$+\frac{1}{7} - \frac{1}{8} = \frac{1}{56}$

$q_1 = \frac{1/30}{1/12} = 2,5$

$q_2 = \frac{1/60}{1/56} = 1,0\ldots$

$q_3 = \frac{1/240}{1/182} = 1,32$

$\lim q = \lim_{n\to\infty} \frac{a_{n+1}}{a_n} = 1$

Unentschieden!

2.) $\quad 1 - \frac{1}{3} + \frac{1}{5} - \frac{1}{7}\cdots$

$\left[\frac{2}{3} + \frac{2}{35} + \frac{2}{99}\cdots\right]$

$q_1 = \frac{99}{35} = 2,82$

$q_2 = \frac{256}{143} = 1,79$

$\lim q = \lim_{n\to\infty} \frac{a_{n+1}}{a_n} = 1$

Unentschieden!

Entwickle die Potenz e^x in eine Reihe und berechne auf Grund dieser Reihe e auf 6 Dezimalen

$$f(x) = e^x \quad ; \quad f'(x) = e^x \cdot k_e = e^x$$

Für $x = 0$ also

$$f(x) = 1, \quad f'(x) = 1, \quad f''(x) = 1, \quad f'''(x) = 1, \ldots$$

Die Taylorsche Reihe heißt

$$f(x) = f(0) + f'(0)\cdot x + \frac{1}{2}\cdot f''(0) x^2 + \frac{1}{3!}f'''(0) x^3$$

Mit Einsetzung obiger Werte wird

$$f(x) = 1 + x + \frac{x^2}{2} + \frac{x^3}{3!} + \frac{x^4}{4!}\cdots$$

Nun ist $e = e^x$, wenn $x = 1$, also

$$f(x) = e = 1 + 1 + \frac{1}{2} + \frac{1}{3!} + \frac{1}{4!}\cdots$$

$$e = 1 + 1 + 0,5 + 0,1664 + 0,0417 + 0,00833 + 0,00159 + 0,0001987 = 2,7182637\cdots$$

$$\text{Entwickle die Funktion}$$
$$y = a^x$$
$$\text{in eine Potenzreihe.}$$
$$f(x) = a^x = (e^{\ln a})^x = e^{\ln a \cdot x}$$
$$\text{Wir setzen } \ln a \cdot x = v \text{ und er-}$$
$$\text{halten } f(v) = e^v. \text{ Es ist also auch}$$
$$f'(x) = e^v;\ f''(x) = e^v;\ f'''(x) = e^v \cdots$$
$$\text{Durch Einsetzung in die Taylorreihe}$$
$$\text{sein } f(x) = f(0) + f'(0) x + \frac{1}{2!} f''(0) x^2 \ldots$$
$$\text{Der Ableitung } f^{(n)}(x) \text{ für } x = 0 \text{ entsteht}$$
$$f(v) = 1 + 1 \cdot v + \frac{1}{2} v^2 + \frac{1}{3!} v^3 + \cdots$$
$$\text{Es ist also}$$
$$a^x = f(x) = 1 + x \cdot \ln a + \frac{(x \cdot \ln a)^2}{2} + \frac{(x \cdot \ln a)^3}{3!} \cdots$$

Unendliche Reihen.

$$\text{Die folgende Reihe ist gliedweise zu}$$
$$\text{differenzieren und ein allgemeiner}$$
$$\text{Ausdruck für } c_1, c_2 \text{ usw. zu ermitteln.}$$

$$f(x) = c_0 + c_1 \cdot x + c_2 \cdot x^2 + c_3 x^3 + \cdots + c_m \cdot x^m$$
$$f'(x) = c_1 + 2c_2 x + 3c_3 x^2 + 4c_4 x^3 + \cdots + m \cdot c_m x^{m-1}$$
$$f''(x) = 2c_2 + 6c_3 x + 12c_4 x^2 + \cdots + (m-1) m c_m x^{m-2}$$
$$f'''(x) = 6c_3 + 24c_4 x + \cdots + (m-2)(m-1) m c_m x^{m-3}$$
$$f^{(m)}(x) = [m-(m-1)] \cdot [m-(m-2)] \cdot [m-(m-3)] \cdots [m-2] \cdot [m-1] m c_m x^{m-m}$$
$$= 1 \cdot 2 \cdot 3 \cdot 4 \cdots (m-2)(m-1) m c_m$$
$$= m! \, c_m$$
$$c_m = \frac{f^{(m)}(x)}{m!}; \quad c_2 = \frac{f''(x)}{2!}; \quad c_{27} = \frac{f^{(27)}(x)}{27!}$$

Extracts from von Braun's notebook in mathematics at the Technische Hochschule Charlottenburg, from where he graduated with a B.Sc. in aeronautical engineering in the spring of 1932. His exercises in geometry and mathematics (infinite series) of 5 May 1931 show how diligently and conscientiously the young student devoted himself to his studies. On his report card (below left), von Braun received average grades (equivalent to B and C in a widely used system in the United States today) for his achievements in mathematics, mechanical and electrical engineering, materials, thermodynamics, and basic economy. At the time, there were two kinds of institutes of higher learning in Germany: the Universität (university) and the Technische Hochschule (roughly, institute of technology). Von Braun studied at the Berlin-Charlottenburg institute from 1930 to 1932 when, upon the urging of Professor Karl Becker, he enrolled in the Friedrich-Wilhelm-Universität Berlin later that year. He received his Ph.D. there in 1934.

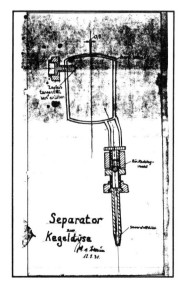

Sketch of a "separator," a component of the "conical rocket motor" invented by Hermann Oberth in 1930.

Wernher von Braun, center, with colleagues Rudolf Nebel, left, and
Kurt Heinisch, right, at the Raketenflugplatz (rocket flying field)
in Berlin-Reinickendorf. During 1930, von Braun spent
nearly all his spare time at the field working on primitive
rockets.

Flying was still another area that captivated von
Braun, who by the age of 21, had received his
pilot's license. This picture appeared on license
No. 663 dated 20 September 1933, and issued in
the Charlottenburg section of Berlin. As early as
1931, von Braun had taken glider lessons at the
Grunau Soaring Center under Wolf Hirth; and, in
1932, started regular flying lessons there, graduating
with the aviatrix Hanna Reitsch.

Rocket experimenters in Berlin, 1930. Left to right: Rudolf Nebel; Dr. Alexander Ritter from the Chemisch-Technische Reichsanstalt, Berlin; Hans Bermüller; Kurt Heinisch; Hermann Oberth; two unidentified men standing behind Oberth; Klaus Riedel; Wernher von Braun; and another unidentified man.

Von Braun's mentor, spaceflight pioneer Hermann Oberth (1894-1989), seen working on a liquid propellant rocket engine in 1929. In the 1920s, Oberth published two basic works that influenced an entire generation of German rocket experimenters and space enthusiasts.

13

digkeiten und γ, γ_1 die entsprechenden spezifischen Gewichte darstellen. Sind zwei Querschnitte unendlich benachbart, so ist

$$f + df = f_1 \qquad c + dc = c_1 \qquad \gamma + d\gamma = \gamma_1$$

also

$$f\,c\,\gamma = (f + df)\,(c + dc)\,(\gamma + d\gamma)$$

Ausmultipliziert nach Herausstreichen der Differentiale 2. Ord-

QVOD FELIX FAVSTVMQVE SIT

VNIVERSITATIS LITTERARIAE
FRIDERICAE GVILELMAE
BEROLINENSIS

RECTORE MAGNIFICO

EUGEN FISCHER

MEDICINAE DOCTORE IN HAC VNIVERSITATE PROFESSORE PVBLICO ORDINARIO RECTORE INSTITVTI A GVILELMO
IMPERATORE AD STVDIA RERVM HVMANARVM PROVLGANDAS PROCREANDASQVE AVCENDA CONDITI

EX DECRETO ORDINIS AMPLISSIMI PHILOSOPHORVM
PROMOTOR LEGITIME CONSTITVTVS

ORDINIS PHILOSOPHORVM H. T. DECANVS

WILHELM HORN

PHILOSOPHIAE DOCTORE IN HAC VNIVERSITATE PROFESSORE PVBLICO ORDINARIO SEMINARII ANGLICI DIRECTORE

VIRO CLARISSIMO ATQVE DOCTISSIMO

WERNHER FREIHERR VON BRAUN

IN OPPIDO CVI NOMEN EST WIRSITZ IN PROVINCIA POSNANIA NATO
POSTQVAM EXAMEN PHILOSOPHICVM CVM LAVDE SVSTINVIT
ET DISSERTATIONEM SVPRAM CVIVS TITVLVS EST

„ÜBER BRENNVERSVCHE"

AVCTORITATE ORDINIS PROBATAM EDIDIT

PHILOSOPHIAE DOCTORIS
ET ARTIVM LIBERALIVM MAGISTRI

ORNAMENTA ET HONORES

DIE XXVII M. IVLII A. MCMXXXIV

RITE CONTVLIT

COLLATAQVE PVBLICO HOC DIPLOMATE

PHILOSOPHORVM ORDINIS OBSIGNATIONE COMPROBATO

DECLARAVIT

Konstruktive, theoretische und experimentelle Beiträge

zu dem Problem der

Flüssigkeitsrakete

DISSERTATION

zur Erlangung der Würde eines

Dr. phil.

der Friedrich-Wilhelms-Universität zu Berlin

Vorgelegt am 16. April 1934 von

WERNHER FREIHERR VON BRAUN

aus Berlin

Beim Raketenofen ist nun im ganzen Düsenbereich abnehmender Druck, dp somit unter allen Umständen negativ. Die Frage, ob das Element $\dfrac{df_i}{f}$ der Querschnittsveränderung positiv oder negativ ist, ob die Düse also konvergent oder divergent verlaufen muß, hängt also ausschließlich von dem Glied in der Klammer ab.

Hier sind nun drei Fälle möglich:

1. $\dfrac{g\,v}{c^2} > \dfrac{1}{\varkappa\,p}$. Dann ist die Klammer positiv, $\dfrac{df}{f}$ negativ; die Düse muß also in dem Strömgeschwindigkeitsbereich $c > \sqrt{g\,\varkappa\,p\,v}$ konvergent verlaufen.

2. $\dfrac{g\,v}{c^2} < \dfrac{1}{\varkappa\,p}$. Hier wird $\dfrac{df}{f}$ positiv, die Strömgeschwindigkeit in dem Bereich $c > \sqrt{g\,\varkappa\,p\,v}$ erfordert also einen divergenten Düsenverlauf.

3. $\dfrac{g\,v}{c^2} = \dfrac{1}{\varkappa\,p}$. Für diesen zwischen 1. und 2. liegenden Fall wird $\dfrac{df}{f} = 0$. Das bedeutet: Wird die Strömgeschwindigkeit $c = \sqrt{g\,\varkappa\,p\,v}$ erreicht, so muß gerade dort der Übergang vom konvergenten in den divergenten Düsenteil, d. h. die engste Stelle der Düse, liegen.

Man kann nun auch umgekehrt folgern: Da dp, wie sich übrigens auch durch einfache Messung nachweisen läßt, während des Expansionsverlaufes niemals Null werden kann, muß bei jeder Ausströmung von Gasen im engsten Querschnitt („Düsenhals") die Geschwindigkeit sich auf den Wert

$$c_m = \sqrt{g\,\varkappa\,p_m\,v_m} \qquad (21a)$$

einstellen, sofern nur die Expansion ohne Zu- und Abführung von Wärme, also adiabatisch, verläuft. Diese Geschwindigkeit stellt die Schallgeschwindigkeit des betreffenden Gases bei dem Halsdruck p_m und dem zugehörigen spez. Volumen v_m dar. Wegen der Zustandsgleichung kann man natürlich auch schreiben:

$$c_m = \sqrt{g\,\varkappa\,R\,T_m} \; . \qquad (21b)$$

c_m ist also vom Ofendruck unabhängig.

Es ist nun noch von Interesse, auch den Druck p_m im Düsenhals zu kennen. Setzt man in unserer Gl. (12a) anstelle des Mündungsdruckes p_a den Halsdruck p_m ein, so erhält man die Geschwindigkeit, die sich bei adiabatischer Expansion von p_i auf p_m entwickeln kann. Dieser Ausdruck muß natürlich mit ... ein. Durch Gleichsetzen wird

$$\ldots = 2g\,\frac{\varkappa}{\varkappa - 1}\,p_i\,v_i\left[1 - \left(\frac{p_m}{p_i}\right)^{\frac{\varkappa - 1}{\varkappa}}\right]$$

$p_m\,v_m^{\varkappa}$ ist auch

$$\ldots^{\frac{1}{\varkappa}} = \frac{2}{\varkappa - 1}\,p_i\,v_i\left[1 - \left(\frac{p_m}{p_i}\right)^{\frac{\varkappa - 1}{\varkappa}}\right]$$

$$\left(\frac{\ldots}{}\right)^{\frac{\varkappa - 1}{\varkappa}}\left(1 + \frac{2}{\varkappa - 1}\right) = \frac{2}{\varkappa - 1} \; ;$$

$$\frac{p_m}{p_i} = \left(\frac{2}{\varkappa + 1}\right)^{\frac{\varkappa}{\varkappa - 1}} \; . \qquad (22)$$

...che Druckverhältnis" ist also ausschließlich ... p_i und p_m leicht meßbar sind, ist hier so...he Möglichkeit gegeben, einen Einblick in ... vor Eintritt in die Lavaldüse zu tun. Auf ...erdurch Rückschlüsse auf den wahren Ver...m Ofen zu ziehen, soll in einem der näch...rückgegriffen werden.

$$\ldots\right)^{\frac{\varkappa - 1}{\varkappa}}$$ wird die Temperatur im Düsenhals

$$T_m = \frac{2}{\varkappa + 1}\,T_i \; . \qquad (23)$$

Setzt man z. B. $\varkappa = 1{,}2$, so wird

$$p_m = 0{,}564\,p_i$$

und

$$T_m = 0{,}91\,T_i \; .$$

Jetzt ist noch eine Beziehung erforderlich, die es ermöglicht, das Querschnittsverhältnis der Lavaldüse zwischen Düsenhals und Mündung für ein gewünschtes Druckgefälle zu errechnen.

Mit der Kontinuitätsgleichung (16)

$$f_m\,c_m\,\gamma_m = f_a\,c_a\,\gamma_a$$

wird

$$\frac{f_m}{f_a} = \frac{c_a\,\gamma_a}{c_m\,\gamma_m} = \frac{c_a\,v_m}{c_m\,v_a} \; .$$

Durch Einsetzen von Gl. (12a) und (21a) wird weiter

$$\frac{f_m}{f_a} = \frac{v_m}{v_a}\sqrt{\frac{2g\,\dfrac{\varkappa}{\varkappa - 1}\,p_i\,v_i\left[1 - \left(\dfrac{p_a}{p_i}\right)^{\frac{\varkappa - 1}{\varkappa}}\right]}{g\,\varkappa\,p_m\,v_m}}$$

Mit Gl. (22) auch

$$\frac{f_m}{f_a} = \frac{v_m}{v_a}\sqrt{\frac{\dfrac{2}{\varkappa - 1}\,v_i\left[1 - \left(\dfrac{p_a}{p_i}\right)^{\frac{\varkappa - 1}{\varkappa}}\right]}{v_m\left(\dfrac{2}{\varkappa + 1}\right)^{\frac{\varkappa}{\varkappa - 1}}}}$$

Setzt man hierin $\dfrac{v_i}{v_a} = \left(\dfrac{p_a}{p_i}\right)^{\frac{1}{\varkappa}}$, so wird nach einigen Umformungen

$$\frac{f_m}{f_a} = \left(\frac{\varkappa + 1}{2}\right)^{\frac{1}{\varkappa - 1}}\left(\frac{p_a}{p_i}\right)^{\frac{1}{\varkappa}}\sqrt{\frac{\varkappa + 1}{\varkappa - 1}\left[1 - \left(\frac{p_a}{p_i}\right)^{\frac{\varkappa - 1}{\varkappa}}\right]} \; . \qquad (24)$$

Mit dieser Gleichung läßt sich für jedes Druckgefälle des Querschnittsverhältnis der Lavaldüse errechnen. Die Einfachheit der Ermittlung halber ist in Tafel 5 diese Funktion für einige Werte von $\varkappa$ (bzw. n, vgl. später) aufgetragen.

Extracts from the doctoral dissertation on "Structural, Theoretical, and Experimental Contributions to the Problem of the Liquid-Propellant Rocket" by Wernher Freiherr von Braun, awarded in 1934 by the Friedrich-Wilhelm -Universität, Berlin. His dissertation was probably the first paper to analyze and discuss the interrelationships between pressure, temperature, flow velocity, gas parameters, and basic physical constants in a rocket motor in a concise yet rather complete fashion. Von Braun based his dissertation largely on his own experimental and theoretical work.

14

Rudolf Nebel, left, and 18-year-old von Braun, right, carry their Mirak rockets at Raketenflugplatz, Berlin-Reinickendorf.

Von Braun, by now 24 years old, is photographed in his Luftwaffe cadet uniform. Like virtually all young men in Germany at the time, von Braun put in time with the armed forces, earning a military pilot's license before returning to developing rockets at Kummersdorf.

II

The Kummersdorf and Peenemünde Years

1932-1945

Wernher von Braun and Director of Training Karl Casper await visitors from Kummersdorf at the Zinnowitz railway station for a tour and social gathering at Peenemünde, 1938. Construction at the rocket development center had begun two years earlier; by April 1937, von Braun and most of his team members had moved up from Kummersdorf.

Wernher von Braun at his desk in the building designated *Haus 4*, Peenemünde shortly after having moved there in 1937 from Kummersdorf.

Fighter ace and commander-in-chief of the Luftwaffe fighter arm from 1941-1945, Major General Adolf Galland, center with moustache, inspects the Peenemünde center in 1943. Galland flew some 300 missions with the Condor Legion during the Spanish Civil War and is credited with more than 100 victories in World War II. To his right with hands in pockets stands von Braun.

Wernher von Braun enjoys a break from work with Chief Staff Physician Dr. Ernst Bahr as they sail in the Baltic Sea near Peenemünde during the summer of 1942. Moments such as this were all too rare during World War II.

Army Colonels Walter Dornberger and Leo Zanssen stroll leisurely in Berlin during the summer of 1942 with Drs. Walter Thiel, head of A-4 missile propulsion development, and Wernher von Braun.

Colonel Walter Dornberger, without longcoat, briefs officers on Peenemünde developments in mid-July 1942. Behind him in civilian clothes is Wernher von Braun.

Group picture taken in 1942 at Peenemünde on the occasion of the visit of executives from the Luftschiffbau Zeppelin in Friedrichshafen, at the time being considered as a site for the assembly of A-4 missiles. Left to right, *front row:* Major Gerhard Stegmeier; Dr. Ernst Dürr, chief engineer at the Zeppelin works; Dr. Hugo Eckener, head of Zeppelin; Colonel Walter Dornberger and Dr. Wernher von Braun; *second row:* Franz Miller, administrative director at Zeppelin; an unidentified man (just to the left of Dornberger) who was Zeppelin's plant superintendent; Dr. Walter Thiel; and next to him Captain Heinz Stölzel; *back row:* unidentified officer; Hugo Eckener's son Knut Eckener; Captain Otto Stetter; Eberhard Rees; Dr. Rudolf Hermann; and Dr. Hermann Kurzweg.

Wernher von Braun's deputy, Eberhard Rees; von Braun; and Fritz Steinhoff at Peenemünde. The latter was the brother of top von Braun associate Ernst Steinhoff and commander of the submarine U 511 from which rocket launching tests were made in 1942.

An A-4 rocket explodes on Test Stand VII, Peenemünde, 7 January 1943. Failures preceded and followed the first successful A-4 launch on 3 October 1942.

Aerial view of the engineering and development area of Peenemünde photographed by the Royal Air Force in July 1943. In the center of the photo are *Haus 4* where von Braun had his office; *Haus 5*, the guest house; *Haus 30*, bachelors' quarters; and the Army headquarters office of Dornberger and Zanssen. To the left are three-story-high machine shop facilities from whose roof missile launches were often observed, the computing area, the wind-tunnel design offices, and the aerodynamic facility. To the right in the photo are the offices of Baugruppe Schlempp and the planning and design offices for the *Werk Süd* A-4 preproduction facility.

Group photograph at Peenemünde. Left to right: unidentified officer; Major Heigel; Colonel Gerhard Stegmeier, chief of the A-4 preproduction works; Ministerial Councillor Godomar Schubert, his works manager; Colonel Kamenitzky; Wernher von Braun; Stabsintendant Staden; unidentified officer; Chief Staff Physician Dr. Ernst Bahr; and Captain Otto Stetter.

VIP visit to Peenemünde on 26 May 1943. At the extreme left is Dr. Walter Thiel, von Braun's propulsion chief, and next to him is Councillor Plendel. The officer behind him is Colonel and staff officer Claus Count Schenk von Stauffenberg who two years later would make an unsuccessful attempt on Hitler's life. Further to the right walks Infantry General Herbert Olbricht, an unidentified officer, and then Grand Admiral Karl Dönitz in the naval greatcoat. Behind Dönitz in civilian hat is Paul Storch. General Heinz Brandt is seen in front of the A-4, hands behind his back. Colonel Walter Dornberger has turned to talk to the officer behind him while Wernher von Braun in dark suit follows to his left. Officer at extreme right is unidentified.

Walter Dornberger, Gerhard Stegmeier, Walter Thiel, Wernher von Braun, and Leo Zanssen confer in front of an A-4 at Peenemünde in 1943.

A moment of relaxation in Peenemünde, c. 1943. Left to right: Hermann Kröger, Ludwig Roth, Wernher von Braun, Walter Dornberger, Werner Gengelbach, and Ernst Steinhoff.

Visit to Peenemünde in 1943 by General Walter von Axthelm, head of antiaircraft ("flak"), to discuss surface-to-air missile developments. To his left are Dornberger and von Braun.

In November 1944, Wernher von Braun was awarded a *Kriegsverdienstkreuz I. Klasse mit Schwertern* (War Service Cross, First Class, with swords) in recognition of his work on the A-4. To his right enjoying dinner in the Offizierskasino at Peenemünde are Major General Dornberger (who had been promoted from Colonel in July 1943), a *Ritterkreuz* (Knight's Cross) recipient the same evening; and to his left Major General Erwin Rossmann. Von Braun lifts a cup in the center picture while Dornberger holds a paper in his hands. At

bottom, von Braun delivers remarks appropriate to the occasion. To his right are Dornberger, Colonel Gerhard Stegmeier, and Dipl.-Ing. Karl Brützel. To von Braun's immediate left is Rossmann, and next to him Ministerial Councillor Godomar Schubert.

In April 1945, von Braun, Dornberger, and their colleagues (including some 100 military personnel) found lodging here in Haus Ingeburg in Oberjoch near Hindelang, waiting for the opportunity to make contact with American forces advancing into Bavaria from

Austria. The war ended for Peenemünde's leaders in early May when contact was made with elements of the 324th Infantry Regiment, U.S. 44th Infantry Division.

Magnus von Braun (left) and his brother Wernher (right) in front of a restaurant in Reutte, Austria, shortly after surrendering to the 324th Infantry Regiment in May 1945. Standing, center, is Pfc. Frederick P. Schneikert, who made the initial contact with the von Brauns and their colleagues who had been staying in Oberjoch's Haus Ingeburg just across the border in southern Germany.

Hans Hüter, left, and Wernher von Braun, right, prepare to board an American C-47 aircraft in Munich, July 1945. Following interrogations in Garmisch, Paris, and London, von Braun left for the United States in September to begin a new chapter in rocket history.

III

*Transfer to America: Fort Bliss
and White Sands*

1945-1950

Von Braun and some teammates enjoy a weekend outing at the Billy the Kid bar and museum, Lincoln, New Mexico, 1946. From left to right: Walter Burose, Herbert Guendel, Willi Mrazek, Friedrich Dhom, Emil Hellebrand, Walter Jacobi, Hermann Weidner, Helmut Zoike, Wernher von Braun, Robert Paetz, and Oscar Bauschinger.

Paperclip specialists renovated and regularly frequented this clubhouse during the immediate postwar years, which they spent at Fort Bliss following their arrival from Germany.

The Paperclip team's clubhouse and garden trellises at Fort Bliss in 1946.

Scientific instruments are checked and calibrated aboard a V-2, which is being prepared for flight in 1946 at the White Sands Proving Ground, New Mexico. During the ensuing years, some 70 V-2s restored and converted to conduct upper atmospheric research were fired from White Sands. Courtesy Dr. Richard Tousey, Naval Research Laboratory.

A V-2 with its scientific payload aboard is now ready for launch at the White Sands Proving Ground, New Mexico, in 1946. The first attempt to fire a converted V-2 in April 1946 fails, the second in May is partially successful, and the third sent off on 28 June reaches 67 miles altitude and is hailed a full success. Courtesy Dr. Richard Tousey, Naval Research Laboratory.

Converted V-2 upper atmosphere sounding
rocket on its *Meillerwagen* erecting trailer at
White Sands. Courtesy Erich W. Neubert.

Drs. Martin Schilling, Wernher von Braun, and Ernst Steinhoff (left to right) inspect a
V-2 rocket motor at the White Sands Proving Ground, New Mexico, in 1946.

Major James P. Hamill, left, and von Braun, right, at Fort Bliss, Texas, 1946. Hamill was assigned the job of coordinating the work of the Germans and serving as their day-to-day leader at Fort Bliss and White Sands. When Hamill accompanied von Braun by train to El Paso from Washington in October 1945, he later complained: "Since I came back from Europe, instead of being allowed to go and see my wife, I've been made to honeymoon with von Braun."

American rocket specialist George P. Sutton meets with Wernher von Braun and teammates at Fort Bliss in 1950. Left to right: Walther Riedel, Tom Myers, Doug Hege, von Braun, Sutton, and Alfred Africano.

IV

The Redstone Years

1950-1960

Pictured left to right: Wernher von Braun; Dr. Richard W. Porter, General Electric Company; and Colonel Carroll D. Hudson, commander of Redstone Arsenal in 1950 shortly after the von Braun team arrived in Huntsville, Alabama, from Fort Bliss, Texas. Porter had played a key role in contacting and interrogating the team in Germany and helping the paperclip individuals to settle in the United States after the war. Courtesy U.S. Army Ordnance, Redstone Arsenal.

Von Braun water-boarding on the Tennessee River near Guntersville, Alabama, in 1951. Next to flying, von Braun's favorite pastime was water sports. For years he kept a houseboat as well as a speedboat for weekend relaxation.

Participants at the *Collier's* magazine symposium in New York City in early 1952 that led to the publication of a seminal eight-article series on space travel. Left to right, science writer and rocket expert Willy Ley; Dr. Fred L. Whipple, chairman, Department of Astronomy, Harvard University; von Braun; artists Chesley Bonestell, Rolf Klep, and Fred Freeman; and Cornelius Ryan, series editor as well as associate editor at *Collier's*.

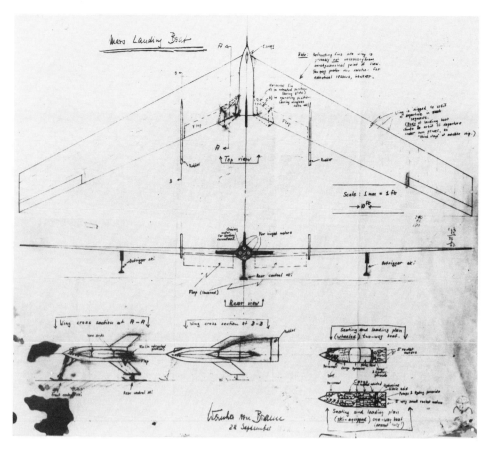

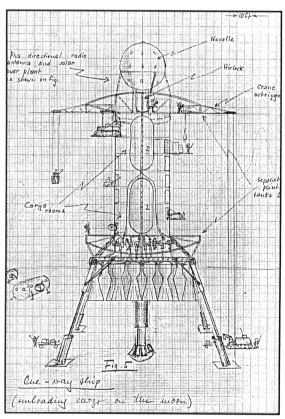

In 1952, von Braun executed this drawing of what he termed a "Mars landing boat" to guide artists illustrating his series of articles in the now defunct *Collier's* magazine. Seen are the wing outline and interior layouts of the plans for seating and loading. Paintings of the "boat" were later made by Chesley Bonestell and Fred Freeman.

Original von Braun drawing of a lunar cargo ship, with callouts, described in his article "The Journey" in *Collier's* magazine's *Man on the Moon* series, 18 October 1952. The rendering was made in June 1952 in pencil on Keuffel and Esser aqua engineering graph paper.

Von Braun visits the Naval Ordnance Laboratory, White Oak, Maryland, on 19 March 1952 to deliver an address to members and guests of the American Rocket Society's Washington-Baltimore Section. More than 2,000 persons were on hand, filling the auditorium and adjacent corridors where speakers were installed. So popular was the occasion that a large number of persons had to be turned away. Left to right: Frederick C. Durant III, ARS vice president; von Braun; Willy Ley; Harry J. Archer, president of the ARS section; and ARS general counsel Andrew G. Haley. In the foreground are models of von Braun's three-stage launch vehicle.

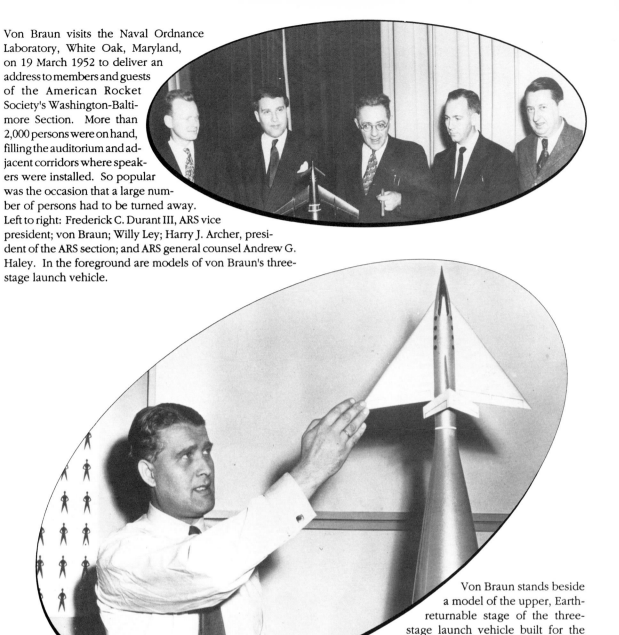

Von Braun stands beside a model of the upper, Earth-returnable stage of the three-stage launch vehicle built for the Walt Disney spaceflight series in the mid-1950s. Courtesy Dr. Carsbie C. Adams.

Harvard Professor Fred L. Whipple, right, and von Braun converse with Trans World Airlines vice-president of engineering Hal Hibbard, left, and TWA president Ralph S. Damon at the Second Symposium on Space Travel held in October 1952 in New York's American Museum of Natural History-Hayden Planetarium.

41

Major Paul O. Siebeneichen, chief, Guided Missile Development Division, Redstone Arsenal; Major General John F. Uncles, deputy assistant chief of staff, G-4 (logistics), Research and Development, U.S. Army; von Braun; Brigadier General Thomas K. Vincent, commanding general, Redstone Arsenal, and Brigadier General Holger N. Toftoy, deputy commanding general, Redstone Arsenal, Huntsville, Alabama. Courtesy U.S. Army Ordnance, Redstone Arsenal.

Dr. Heinz Haber, von Braun, and Willy Ley with model of a Personal Space Maneuvering Unit at the Walt Disney Studios, July 1954. Von Braun often referred to the unit as a "bottle suit." Shortly before this picture was taken, Ley wrote von Braun about what he had heard in the corridor following a TV interview: "One piece of public (male) explained to a ditto (female) that you (or I) build rockets under the name Wernher von Braun but that you (or I) write about rockets under the name of Willy Ley. The one thing the gentleman did not know was which one of these two names is the legal name. If you should have a lot of spare time, please figure this out."

Wernher von Braun examines a model of the three-stage launch rocket he designed for a series of articles on space that appeared in *Collier's* magazine in the early 1950s and was subsequently modified for three "Tomorrowland" television programs on spaceflight developed by the Walt Disney Studios in the mid-1950s. The picture was taken in *Colliers's* offices in New York City.

Early planning meeting for the proposed Orbiter satellite held in Washington, D.C., on 17 March 1955. From left to right: *seated*, Commander George W. Hoover, Office of Naval Research; Frederick C. Durant III, Arthur D. Little, Inc.; James B. Kendrick, Aerophysics Development Corporation; William S. Giardini, Alabama Tool and Die Corporation; Philippe W. Newton, Department of Defense; Rudolf H. Schlidt, Army Ballistic Missile Agency; Gerhard Heller, Army Ballistic Missile Agency; and Wernher von Braun, director, Development Operations Division, Army Ballistic Missile Agency; and *standing*, Lieutenant Commander William E. Dowdell, U.S. Navy; Alexander Satin, Office of Naval Research; Commander Robert C. Truax, U.S. Navy; Liston Tatum, IBM Corporation; Austin W. Stanton, Varo, Inc.; Fred L. Whipple, Harvard University; George W. Petri, IBM Corporation; Lowell O. Anderson, Office of Naval Research; and Milton W. Rosen, Naval Research Laboratory. Courtesy Frederick C. Durant III.

Members of the Army Ballistic Missile Agency with a model of the Explorer 1 satellite made in 1957. *Standing*, left to right: Willi Mrazek, Walter Haeussermann, and Stuhlinger; *seated*, left to right: Eberhard Rees, Brigadier General John B. Medaris, and von Braun. Courtesy Mitchell R. Sharpe.

Von Braun, Dr. Carsbie C. Adams, and Ordway during a moment of relaxation at Cocoa Beach, Florida, September 1957.

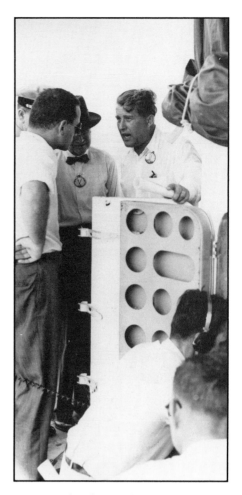

Von Braun briefs guided missile "czar" William M. Holaday at the Air Force Missile Test Center in Florida in mid-May 1956.

Brigadier General John B. Medaris, commander of the U.S. Army Ballistic Missile Agency; von Braun, director, Development Operations Division; and Brigadier General Holger N. Toftoy, commander, U.S. Army Rocket and Guided Missile Agency, Redstone Arsenal. The picture was taken in early 1956. Courtesy U.S. Army Ordnance, Redstone Arsenal.

Von Braun and Stuhlinger work at the observatory of the Rocket City Astronomical Association in Huntsville, Alabama, 1956. Courtesy *The Huntsville Times*/Von Braun Archives.

At the Walt Disney Studios in California, von Braun and Stuhlinger discuss nuclear-electric spaceships designed to undertake missions to the planet Mars. Such vehicles were seen in the last of three television films on space in the "Tomorrowland" series. Entitled "Mars and Beyond," it was first aired in December 1957.

General James van Fleet visits Major General Holger N. Toftoy and von Braun at Redstone Arsenal in 1956.

Celebrating the arrival of the first issue of *Space Journal*, published by Huntsville's Rocket City Astronomical Association, summer of 1957. *Seated*, left to right: Irmgard Stuhlinger, Tilly Oberth, and Maria von Braun; *standing*, left to right: Ernst Stuhlinger, Hermann Oberth and Wernher von Braun. Courtesy U.S. Army Ordnance, Redstone Arsenal.

Von Braun and daughter Iris Careen on horseback at the plantation of Dr. Carsbie C. Adams in Culloden, Georgia, 1957. Courtesy Dr. Carsbie C. Adams.

November 1957 meeting of the National Advisory Committee for Aeronautics' Special Committee on Space Technology in Washington, D.C. Left to right: Edward R. Sharp, Colonel Norman C. Appold, Abraham Hyatt, Dr. Hendrick W. Bode, Dr. Randolph Lovelace, Samuel K. Hoffman, Dr. Milton V. Clauser, H. Julian Allen, Dr. Robert R. Gilruth, James R. Dempsey, Carl B. Palmer, Committee chairman Dr. H. Guyford Stever, Dr. Hugh Dryden, Dale R. Corson, Dr. Abraham Silverstein, and Dr. Wernher von Braun.

Army Ballistic Missile Agency commander Major General John Bruce Medaris with members of the original von Braun Peenemünde team in 1957. From left to right: Stuhlinger, Friedrich von Saurma, Fritz Mueller, Hermann Weidner, Erich Neubert, Willi Mrazek, Karl Heimburg, Arthur Rudolph, Fritz Weber, von Braun, Oswald Lange, Medaris, Helmut Hoelzer, Hans Maus, Ernst Geissler, and Hans Hueter. Next to Hueter is George Constant, who was not a member of the Peenemünde team. Courtesy U. S. Army Ordnance, Redstone Arsenal.

Secretary of Defense Charles E. Wilson awards six individuals the Distinguished Civilian Service Medal in 1957 at the Pentagon, Washington, D.C. Left to right: Dr. Harvey Krutter, Dr. F. Reed Dickerson, Otto Walcher, Secretary Wilson, von Braun, Robert E. Meidel, and Dr. Maurice A. Hilleman. Courtesy Department of Defense.

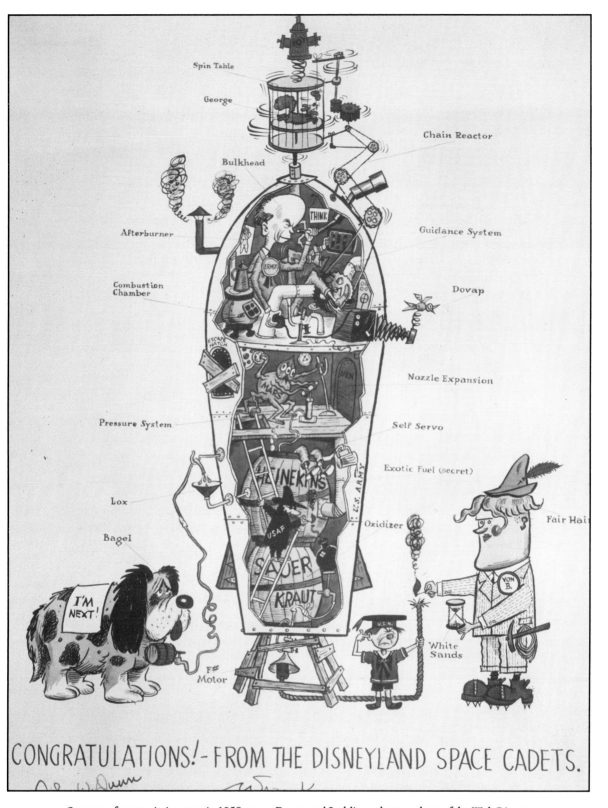

The following labels appear in the cartoon:

Spin Table
George
Chain Reactor
Bulkhead
Afterburner
Guidance System
Combustion Chamber
Dovap
Pressure System
Nozzle Expansion
Self Servo
Exotic Fuel (secret)
Lox
Oxidizer
Bagel
Fair Hair
THINK
ERNST
HEINEKINS
U.S. ARMY
USAF
SAUER KRAUT
MEN
MARS
I'M NEXT!
VON B.
V.F.N.
White Sands
F# Motor

CONGRATULATIONS! - FROM THE DISNEYLAND SPACE CADETS.

Cartoon of appreciation sent in 1958 to von Braun and Stuhlinger by members of the Walt Disney Studios who worked on the "Tomorrowland" space series in the mid-1950s. Fair-haired von Braun appears at lower right while Stuhlinger above in the nose cone is presumably in the process of thinking.

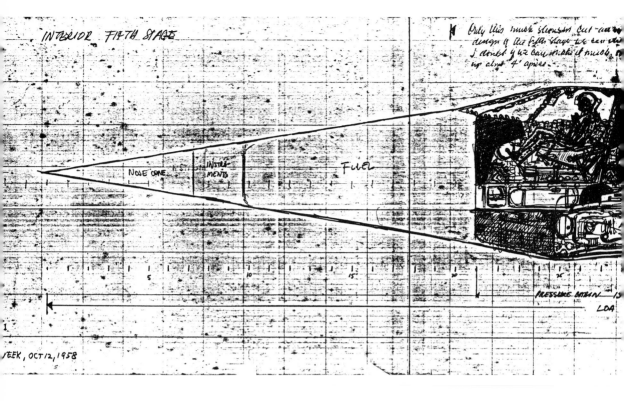

This drawing on engineering graph paper, which was rendered by artist-collaborator Fred Freeman with annotations by von Braun, depicts the interior of the manned upper stage of a Moon rocket. Revealed is the pressure cabin in cutaway with its contour seats, astrodome, and airlocks. Aft of the control cabin are fuel tanks and rocket motors; forward, the nose cone, instruments, and additional propellant. The illustration was published in the 12 October 1958 issue of *This Week* magazine and later (in 1960) was signed by Freeman.

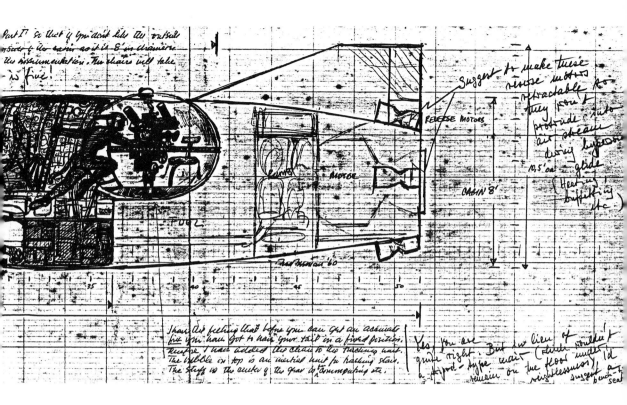

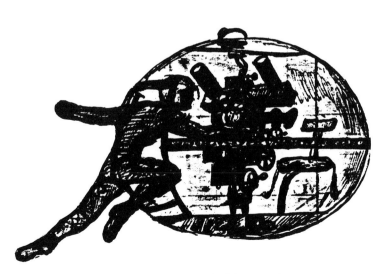

Detail of the astrodome.

Dr. Ernst Stuhlinger, center, receives an award from Brigadier General John A. Barclay, left, in 1958 accompanied by von Braun, right.

Von Braun shares broadcasting booth with Edward R. Murrow of CBS in 1958.

Professor Hermann Oberth and von Braun are briefed on satellite orbits by Dr. Charles A. Lundquist in mid-June 1958 at the Army Ballistic Missile Agency, Redstone Arsenal, Huntsville, Alabama.

Walter Wiesman, left, and von Braun at the opening of the film *I Aim at the Stars* at Loew's Palace Theatre in Washington, D.C., 28 September 1960. The premiere was sponsored by the Army Distaff Foundation to raise funds to establish a residence for widows of Army officers. Among those attending were Mrs. Dwight D. Eisenhower and Army Chief of Staff General George H. Decker. The role of von Braun as an adult was played by Curt Jurgens while Gunther Mruwka played the boyhood scenes. Courtesy Morningside-Worldwide Pictures Production/Columbia Pictures Corporation/Von Braun Archives.

Von Braun visits his parents in Germany following the successful launch of Explorer 1 on 31 January 1958. Left to right: Baroness Emmy von Braun, Baron Magnus von Braun, and Dr. Wernher von Braun. Courtesy Lutz Kleinhans, Frankfurt-Main/Von Braun Archives.

Dr. William H. Pickering, director of the Jet Propulsion Laboratory; Dr. James A. Van Allen, head of the team at Iowa State University responsible for instrumentation; and von Braun, director of Development Operations Division, Army Ballistic Missile Agency, at the National Academy of Sciences in Washington after the successful launch of Explorer 1. As part of the celebration, the three men lift a replica of the satellite. Courtesy U.S. Army/Jet Propulsion Laboratory.

Top center: Von Braun with rolled-up paper in his left hand briefs the seven original Mercury astronauts in ABMA's Fabrication Laboratory, 1959. Left to right: Walter Schirra, Alan Shepard, John Glenn, Scott Carpenter, and L. Gordon Cooper. Blocked by Glenn and von Braun are Virgil Grissom and Donald Slayton.

Top right: Air Force Major General Donald R. Ostrander, on assignment at NASA as launch vehicle director; von Braun; his deputy Eberhard Rees; and Army Brigadier General John Barclay, at Cape Canaveral, Florida, in 1959. Courtesy U.S. Army Ordnance, Redstone Arsenal.

Bottom right: Erik Bergaust, a close friend and editor of the trade magazine *Missiles & Rockets*, interviews von Braun in his office at Redstone Arsenal.

Middle: NASA Administrator Dr. T. Keith Glennan, Army Ordnance Missile Command commander Major General John B. Medaris, von Braun, and ABMA commander Brigadier General John Barclay pose beside a model of the Saturn launch vehicle at Redstone Arsenal in 1959.

Top left: A tense moment in the Cape Canaveral, Florida blockhouse prior to ordering the launch of a Juno II rocket with its lunar-bound Pioneer 4 payload on 3 March 1959. Left to right: Von Braun, Missile Firing Laboratory director Dr. Kurt Debus, Army Ballistic Missile Agency lab director Dr. Walter Haeussermann, ABMA deputy commander Brigadier General John Barclay, and Karl Sendler of the MFL. Courtesy U.S. Army.

Bottom left: ABMA Test Lab director Karl L. Heimburg, von Braun and Major General John B. Medaris, commander, Army Ordnance Missile Command, with an early model of the Saturn launch vehicle, July 1959. Courtesy U.S. Army Ordnance, Redstone Arsenal.

Bottom center: Von Braun, director of ABMA's Development Operations Division, works at his desk in Building 4488, Redstone Arsenal.

In 1959, at a ceremony in Bonn, Wernher von Braun receives the Federal Cross of Merit awarded by the president of the Federal Republic of Germany, Professor Theodor Heuss. With von Braun are brother Sigismund and family. Courtesy Presse und Informationsamt der Bundesregierung—Bundesbildstelle/Von Braun Archives.

Von Braun poses with former Peenemünde team members at the Army Ballistic Missile Agency in Huntsville, June 1959. Left to right: Stuhlinger, Helmut Hoelzer, Karl Heimburg, Ernst Geissler, Erich Neubert, Walter Haeussermann, von Braun, Willi Mrazek, Hans Hueter, Eberhard Rees, Kurt Debus, and Hans Maus. Courtesy U.S. Army Ordnance, Redstone Arsenal.

Medaris, von Braun and Dr. T. Keith Glennan, administrator of the National Aeronautics and Space Administration, stand in front of ABMA headquarters, Redstone Arsenal, 1959. Within a year, the von Braun team will transfer from the Army to NASA. Courtesy U.S. Army Ordnance, Redstone Arsenal.

Von Braun stands with Mrs. Esther C. Goddard, widow of Dr. Robert H. Goddard, beside a model of a large orbital space base in New York City in 1959.

Wernher and Maria von Braun with Soviet academician and leading space personality Leonid I. Sedov at the 11th International Astronautical Congress in Stockholm, 1960.

Von Braun at his desk in 1960 surrounded by rocket models.

The von Brauns vacationing in Florida. Left to right: Wernher, Iris, Margrit, and Maria. Courtesy Bert Henry/Von Braun Archives.

Ordway, left, and von Braun, right, with friend Dr. John D. Moorman enjoy an outdoor lunch at the Ordway home atop Monte Sano, Huntsville, Alabama, November 1960.

Mercury astronauts visit Huntsville in 1960. Sitting around table from the right: Medaris, Virgil I. ("Gus") Grissom, Donald K. ("Deke") Slayton, Walter ("Wally") Schirra, John H. Glenn, Alan B. Shepard, M. Scott Carpenter, Eberhard Rees, L. Gordon Cooper, and Major General John A. Barclay. The man beside him is unidentified. Courtesy U.S. Army Ordnance, Redstone Arsenal.

Negotiations are under way in this picture between officials of the Army Ballistic Missile Agency and those of the National Aeronautics and Space Administration. Seated at left is Dr. T. Keith Glennan, NASA administrator; back to camera is Major General John Barclay, commander of ABMA; and at right are Colonel John G. Zierdt of ABMA and von Braun. Courtesy U.S. Army.

On 13 July 1960, von Braun was the keynote speaker in Auburn, Massachusetts, to commemorate Robert H. Goddard's pioneer liquid propellant rocket flight back in 1926 — the world's first. Standing to von Braun's right is Dr. Richard Porter and to his right are George Sutton and Howard Seiffert, both leading authorities on liquid propellant rocket engines. To von Braun's left are Andrew B. Holmstrom, mayor of Worcester, Massachusetts, and next to him George H. Campbell, town of Auburn selectman.

Von Braun, right, poses beside the Goddard monument. On the other side is Andrew B. Holmstom.

Major General John B. Medaris and von Braun stand in front of the stand built to static-test Redstone and Jupiter missile engines at the time of Medaris's retirement from the Army in January 1960. Courtesy U.S. Army.

President Dwight D. Eisenhower is greeted by Karl Heimburg on the occasion of a tour of Redstone Arsenal and dedication of the new NASA-George C. Marshall Space Flight Center, 8 September 1960. Approaching from the left is Air Force Major General Donald R. Ostrander, director of the NASA Office of Launch Vehicle Programs, and from the right von Braun, newly appointed center director.

Left to right: Alabama Governor John Patterson, Alabama Congressman Carl Elliott, NASA Administrator T. Keith Glennan, Wisconsin Senator Alexander Wiley, Alabama Representative Albert Rains, President Dwight D. Eisenhower, Connecticut Representative Emilio Q. Daddario, Lieutenant General Herbert B. Powell, Alabama Representative Bob Jones, von Braun, Ryan de Graffenried, Army Ordnance Missile Command commander Major General August Schomburg, New York Representative R. Walter Riehlman, Army Chief of Staff General Lyman L. Lemnitzer, and Pennsylvania Representative James G. Fulton. Courtesy U.S. Army Ordnance, Redstone Arsenal.

Dedication of the George C. Marshall Space Flight Center. From left to right: NASA Administrator Dr. T. Keith Glennan, newly appointed center director von Braun, President Eisenhower, Mrs. George C. Marshall, and bust of the late General George C. Marshall. Courtesy U.S. Army Ordnance, Redstone Arsenal.

V

NASA-Marshall Space Flight Center:
The Apollo Drama

1960-1970

Von Braun with close associates in 1961. Left to right: Werner Kuers, Walter Haeussermann, Willi Mrazek, von Braun, Dieter Grau, Oswald Lange, and Erich Neubert.

Von Braun testifying before a congressional committee in Washington, D.C., in 1961. To his left is Dr. Robert C. Seamans, Jr., associate administrator of NASA.

Decatur, Alabama Mayor Murray Dodd, von Braun and Bonnie Holmes, on the occasion of von Braun's nomination as "International Boss of the Year" at the Country Club of Decatur on 16 April 1961.

During von Braun's Huntsville years, 1950 to 1970, he enjoyed spending weekends at Lake Guntersville. Here, von Braun stands near his boat in chest-high water with his daughter Iris, and Ordway with his son Fred.

Von Braun stands with his Mercedes automobile in front of Building 4488 at Redstone Arsenal, Alabama, in 1961. There, both the Army Ballistic Missile Agency and the new NASA-George C. Marshall Space Flight Center shared quarters while the latter's facility was under construction about a mile away.

In November 1961, Wernher von Braun and Carsbie C. Adams were relaxing at the latter's plantation in Culloden, Georgia, when the conversation turned to trips both were planning for the following month. It so happened that von Braun was to deliver some university lectures in Sydney, Australia, early the next year and intended to fly there via Munich, Germany, to visit his father. Adams, in the meantime, had to go to London at about the same time. Suddenly, he recalled, von Braun turned and said "Why don't you come with me and, by golly, we'll just circle the globe!"

They ended up doing just that, starting off together from Atlanta to New York in late December. Von Braun continued on alone to Munich while Adams flew to London. A few days later they met up in Munich and by New Year's Eve 1961 were on the way to India, Nepal, Thailand, and finally Australia. They visited temples and other sites in New Delhi, Banaras, and other centers in India, Kathmandu in Nepal, and the area around Bangkok before reaching their final destination. Courtesy Dr. Carsbie C. Adams.

Von Braun and Adams at India's Fatepuhr Sikri, January 1962.

Von Braun and Adams in Banaras, India, January 1962. Adams recalls that in the Sikh temple, von Braun "behaved just like the natives and sat on the floor with his arms stretched out and then bowed over and put his head on the floor. There he was, barefooted, down on his knees like everyone else."

Von Braun in Kathmandu, Nepal, where he and Adams spent a couple of days in January 1962. Adams relates that von Braun often gave the poor small amounts of cash. "It was typical of his performance," remembers Adams, "his great concern and the kindness he demonstrated. That was one side of von Braun that many people never recognized."

Von Braun in Bangkok, Thailand, January 1962.

On 23 March 1962, von Braun's friends and colleagues in Huntsville help him celebrate his 50th birthday. He and his wife Maria are clearly savoring the moment.

Bart J. Slattery, Jr., NASA-Marshall director of Public Affairs, watches as von Braun cuts the birthday cake with a sword that had just been handed to him.

Von Braun returns the sword to Slattery clearly having enjoyed the cutting ceremony.

Von Braun and Stuhlinger look over a collection of letters, pictures, and notes commemorating von Braun's 50th birthday on 23 March 1962.

Army Ordnance Missile Command commander Major General Francis J. McMorrow, von Braun, President John F. Kennedy, Vice President Lyndon B. Johnson, NASA Administrator James E. Webb, Army Materiel Command commander Lieutenant General F. S. Besson, and Marshall deputy director Eberhard Rees converse beside the Air Force One aircraft that brought the presidential entourage to Redstone Arsenal from Washington, D.C. on 11 September 1962 for a tour of the Marshall Center.   Courtesy U.S. Army Ordnance, Redstone Arsenal.

Kennedy, von Braun, McMorrow, and Johnson at the Redstone Arsenal airstrip shortly after arriving from Washington for the September 1962 tour of Marshall.   Courtesy U.S. Army Ordnance, Redstone Arsenal.

President John F. Kennedy, von Braun, NASA Administrator James E. Webb, Vice President Lyndon B. Johnson, Secretary of Defense Robert S. McNamara, Kennedy's special assistant for Science and Technology Dr. Jerome B. Wiesner, and director of Defense Research and Engineering Dr. Harold Brown tour the George C. Marshall Space Flight Center, 11 September 1962. An impassioned discussion of the best method to travel to the Moon occurred just after this photo was made.

Von Braun; Dr. I. M. Levitt, director of the Fels Planetarium at the Franklin Institute in Philadelphia; and astronaut John H. Glenn in the Sheraton Hotel on the occasion of von Braun's being awarded the Institute's Elliott Cresson Medal. Earlier that same day — 17 October 1962 — Glenn had received the Elisha Kent Gold Medal from the National Geographic Society. Courtesy Dr. I. M. Levitt.

Von Braun receives an advance copy of the book *Astronautical Engineering and Science* in 1963, the year following his 50th birthday — and in its honor. Published by McGraw-Hill, it contained chapters by von Braun's friends and colleagues, many dating back to the 1930s and 1940s. Three of its four editors stand with von Braun in his office; left to right: Dr. George C. Bucher, Ordway, von Braun, and Stuhlinger. Courtesy NASA-Marshall Space Flight Center.

The mayor of Berlin, Willy Brandt, gives a reception in honor of von Braun and professor Hermann Oberth in the City Hall of Schöneberg, Berlin, Germany, on 1 August 1963. Landesbildstelle Berlin/Von Braun Archives.

Von Braun takes a dive in the Neutral Buoyancy Tank at the NASA-Marshall Space Flight Center, assisted by oceanography pioneer Jacques Piccard and Morris W. Hammer. Courtesy NASA-Marshall Space Flight Center.

Michigan Congressman Gerald Ford, who later became U.S. president, being greeted by von Braun in 1963 prior to visiting the NASA-Marshall Space Flight Center.

Von Braun, left, and Dr. Robert R. Gilruth, director of the Manned Spacecraft Center, confer on the Kennedy Space Center landing strip in Florida, 1963.

President John F. Kennedy during a tour of NASA installations at Cape Canaveral, Florida, on 16 November 1963. A week later, he would be assassinated in Dallas, Texas. With him are George E. Mueller, director of the Office of Manned Space Flight (explaining his decision for "all up" testing of Saturn V); George M. Low, program chief for Manned Space Flight; Kurt Debus, director of NASA's Launch Operations Center at the Cape; Robert C. Seamans, Jr., NASA associate administrator; James E. Webb, NASA administrator; President Kennedy; Hugh L. Dryden, NASA deputy administrator; von Braun; Major General Leighton I. Davis, commander, Air Force Missile Test Center at the Cape; and Florida Senator George Smathers. Courtesy NASA–Launch Operations Center.

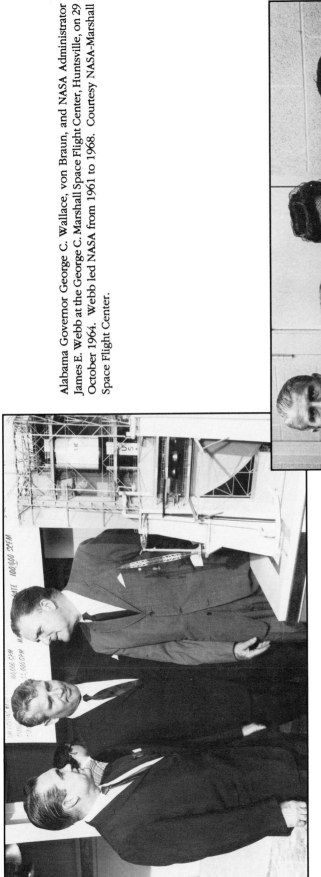

Alabama Governor George C. Wallace, von Braun, and NASA Administrator James E. Webb at the George C. Marshall Space Flight Center, Huntsville, on 29 October 1964. Webb led NASA from 1961 to 1968. Courtesy NASA-Marshall Space Flight Center.

Lady Bird Johnson (right) visits with the von Braun family: Wernher, Iris, Maria, and Margrit, in April 1964.

Von Braun in blockhouse in Florida on the occasion of the Saturn I SA-6 launch on 28 May 1964. Known as the Apollo Mission A-101, it was the first flight of an Apollo spacecraft with a Saturn launch vehicle.

Von Braun, left, and NASA-Kennedy Space Center director Kurt H. Debus, right, discuss the countdown for Saturn I SA-9 flight which carried the Pegasus 1 meteoroid detection satellite into orbit on 16 February 1965.

Von Braun observes the launch of Saturn I SA-8 with its Pegasus 2 payload through a periscope at Kennedy Launch Control Center Complex 27, 25 May 1965. SA-8 was launched after SA-9.

Von Braun visits a school classroom in Huntsville, Alabama, 1965.

Dr. Harry J. Goett, director, Goddard Space Flight Center, and von Braun being congratulated by James E. Webb, George E. Mueller, and Robert C. Seamans, Jr. upon receiving NASA's Outstanding Leadership Awards, October 1964. Courtesy NASA.

Von Braun, left, and Rocco A. Petrone, right, during the launch of Saturn I flight SA-5 at the Kennedy Space Center, Florida, 29 January 1964. This flight was the first of the rocket's Block II configuration and also the first to test the guidance system. Petrone served as Apollo program manager from 1961 to 1966 at which time he became director of Launch Operations until 1969, both positions under Kurt Debus at the Kennedy Space Center.

Willi A. Mrazek; Holger N. Toftoy, Major General, U.S. Army-ret.; and von Braun on the roof of Building 4200, George C. Marshall Space Flight Center on the occasion of a Marshall Center Community Advisory Committee meeting in February 1968. Von Braun holds a model of the Redstone rocket that launched America's first astronaut, Alan B. Shepard, into a ballistic trajectory on 5 May 1961. Courtesy NASA-Marshall Space Flight Center.

Walt Disney visits the George C. Marshall Space Flight Center on 13 April 1965. From left to right: Robert J. Schwinghamer, Gerhard Heller, Walt Disney, unidentified, von Braun, Stuhlinger, Ken O'Connor, and Bill Bosché. Courtesy NASA.

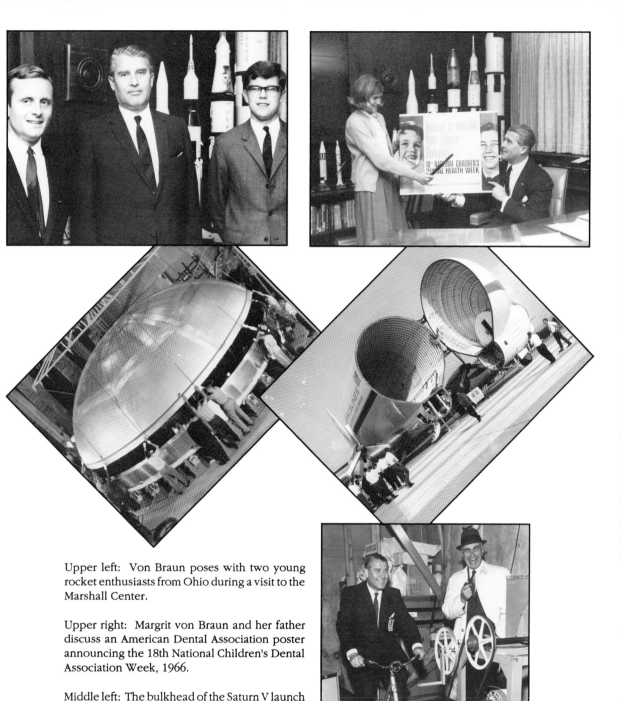

Upper left: Von Braun poses with two young rocket enthusiasts from Ohio during a visit to the Marshall Center.

Upper right: Margrit von Braun and her father discuss an American Dental Association poster announcing the 18th National Children's Dental Association Week, 1966.

Middle left: The bulkhead of the Saturn V launch vehicle first-stage propellant tank is lowered towards the cylindrical portion of the tank at the Boeing company. Courtesy NASA.

Middle right: One of the two "Spacelines" transport planes, one named the *Pregnant Guppy* and the other the *Super Guppy*, built to transport Saturn V third (S-IVB) stages to the Kennedy Space Center.

Lower right: Von Braun tries out an auxiliary generator in a tornado shelter at the NASA-Marshall Space Flight Center as Harry Gorman looks on. Courtesy NASA-Marshall Space Flight Center.

Before going to Antarctica, von Braun and Gilruth took this trip in a jet boat on Waimakariri River in New Zealand, December 1966. Courtesy Mannering and Donaldson, Ltd., Christchurch, New Zealand/Von Braun Archives.

Von Braun during his visit to Antarctica, which lasted from late December 1966 to early January 1967.

Von Braun and companions inspect a New Zealand "Gnat" roving vehicle at that country's Scott Base in Antarctica on 8 January 1967. From left to right: Stuhlinger; von Braun; Colin Clark, leader of Scott Base; and Philip Smith, National Science Foundation.

Von Braun with Colin Clark, leader of New Zealand's Scott Base in Antarctica.

Von Braun at the South Pole on 7 January 1967.

Von Braun, extreme left, and companions frolic around the flagpole at the geographic South Pole in Antarctica while the temperature was minus 25 degrees C (-13 degrees F) 7 January 1967.

Antarctic journey: Colin Clark; Dr. Robert R. Gilruth, director of the Manned Spacecraft Center; and von Braun. Courtesy Robert R. Gilruth.

Von Braun and friends playing around on a pier, Exhuma Island, Bahamas, during a weekend yacht outing with James P. and Lorraine Lewis from Vero Beach, Florida, December 1967.

Von Braun with the Lewises in the Bahamas.

The Apollo Management Council meets at NASA headquarters in Washington, D.C., 1967. Left to right: Von Braun, Dr. Robert R. Gilruth, Dr. George E. Mueller, and Dr. Kurt H. Debus. Courtesy NASA.

Von Braun and his executive secretary of 20 years, Bonnie Holmes, look over the newly published von Braun-Ordway book *History of Rocketry and Space Travel* (New York, Thos. Y. Crowell, 1966).

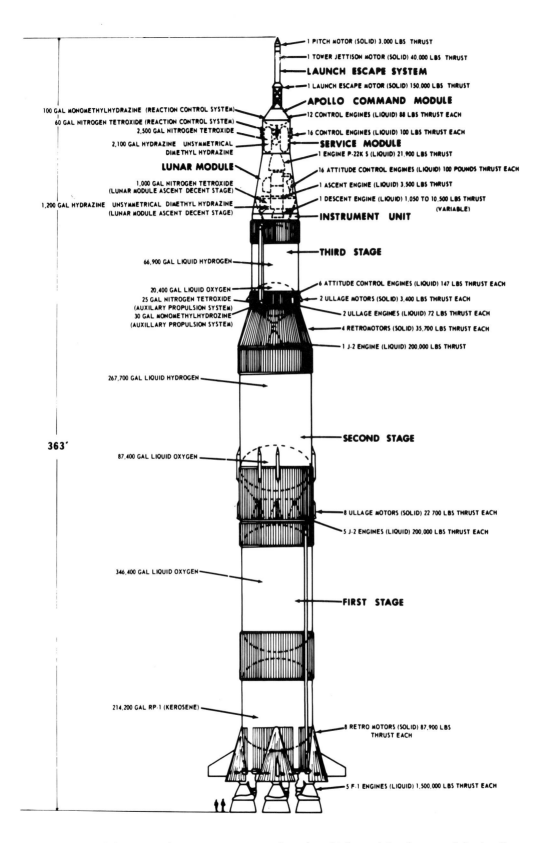

1 PITCH MOTOR (SOLID) 3,000 LBS THRUST

1 TOWER JETTISON MOTOR (SOLID) 40,000 LBS THRUST

LAUNCH ESCAPE SYSTEM

1 LAUNCH ESCAPE MOTOR (SOLID) 150,000 LBS THRUST

APOLLO COMMAND MODULE

100 GAL MONOMETHYLHYDRAZINE (REACTION CONTROL SYSTEM)
60 GAL NITROGEN TETROXIDE (REACTION CONTROL SYSTEM)
2,500 GAL NITROGEN TETROXIDE

12 CONTROL ENGINES (LIQUID) 88 LBS THRUST EACH

16 CONTROL ENGINES (LIQUID) 100 LBS THRUST EACH

2,100 GAL HYDRAZINE UNSYMMETRICAL DIMETHYL HYDRAZINE

SERVICE MODULE

1 ENGINE P-22K S (LIQUID) 21,900 LBS THRUST

LUNAR MODULE

16 ATTITUDE CONTROL ENGINES (LIQUID) 100 POUNDS THRUST EACH

1,000 GAL NITROGEN TETROXIDE
(LUNAR MODULE ASCENT DECENT STAGE)

1 ASCENT ENGINE (LIQUID) 3,500 LBS THRUST

1 DESCENT ENGINE (LIQUID) 1,050 TO 10,500 LBS THRUST

1,200 GAL HYDRAZINE UNSYMMETRICAL DIMETHYL HYDRAZINE
(LUNAR MODULE ASCENT DECENT STAGE)

(VARIABLE)

INSTRUMENT UNIT

THIRD STAGE

66,900 GAL LIQUID HYDROGEN

20,400 GAL LIQUID OXYGEN

6 ATTITUDE CONTROL ENGINES (LIQUID) 147 LBS THRUST EACH

25 GAL NITROGEN TETROXIDE
(AUXILARY PROPULSION SYSTEM)
30 GAL MONOMETHYLHYDROZINE
(AUXILLARY PROPULSION SYSTEM)

2 ULLAGE MOTORS (SOLID) 3,400 LBS THRUST EACH

2 ULLAGE ENGINES (LIQUID) 72 LBS THRUST EACH

4 RETROMOTORS (SOLID) 35,700 LBS THRUST EACH

1 J-2 ENGINE (LIQUID) 200,000 LBS THRUST

267,700 GAL LIQUID HYDROGEN

SECOND STAGE

87,400 GAL LIQUID OXYGEN

363′

8 ULLAGE MOTORS (SOLID) 22,700 LBS THRUST EACH

5 J-2 ENGINES (LIQUID) 200,000 LBS THRUST EACH

346,400 GAL LIQUID OXYGEN

FIRST STAGE

214,200 GAL RP-1 (KEROSENE)

8 RETRO MOTORS (SOLID) 87,900 LBS THRUST EACH

5 F-1 ENGINES (LIQUID) 1,500,000 LBS THRUST EACH

Diagram of the giant three-stage Saturn V launch vehicle and its three-module Apollo spacecraft payload. Courtesy NASA.

An S-II Saturn V second stage is hoisted into its test stand at the Mississippi Test Facility.

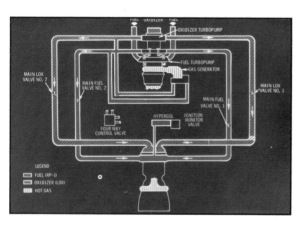

Simplified schematic of the F-1 engine (in a cluster of five, it powered Saturn V's first stage), showing the fuel and oxidizer turbopumps, the gas generators that drive them, fuel and oxidizer feed lines, main valves, and combustion chamber.

The three members of the Saturn family, Saturn I, Saturn IB, and Saturn V. Saturn I relied on a cluster of eight H-1 engines in its first stage and six Centaur RL-10 engines in its second while Saturn IB had the same H-1-based first stage but incorporated a new hydrogen-oxygen J-2 engine in its second stage. Saturn V incorporated a new kerosene-oxygen F-1 cluster for its first stage and J-2 engines in both its second and third stages. Thus, the second stage of Saturn IB became the third stage of Saturn V.

Groundbreaking at the future Alabama Space & Rocket Center, which was carved out of a portion of Redstone Arsenal, 5 August 1968. The center later became known as the U.S. Space & Rocket Center. Von Braun, left, and Major General Charles Eifler, commanding general of the U.S. Army Ordnance Missile Command, do the honors. Courtesy U.S. Space & Rocket Center Archives.

U.S. Space & Rocket Center as it is today. The Saturn V is exhibited in a horizontal position in the foreground, the Saturn IB and other rockets in the center of the photograph. Courtesy U.S. Space & Rocket Center Archives.

Dr. Thomas O. Paine, NASA deputy administrator, examines an ordinary man's shoe outfitted for use in the Saturn I workshop, which later evolved into Skylab. From left to right in workshop mock-up: William Brooksbank, Propulsion and Vehicle Engineering Laboratory at the Marshall Center; von Braun; Colonel Clare F. Farley, executive officer in the Office of the Administrator; and Charles J. Donlan, deputy associate administrator for Manned Space Flight, technical. Courtesy NASA.

Reunion of the von Braun brothers with their father in Oberaudorf, Bavaria, in February 1968. Left to right Magnus, Baron von Braun, Sigismund, and Wernher.

Von Braun and several colleagues and crew members in front of a KC-135 airplane ready to fly through a series of microgravity parabolas, each with a "no-gravity" period of about 20 seconds — "the closest thing to spaceflight a non-astronaut will ever experience."

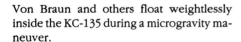

Von Braun, Stuhlinger, and others during a microgravity maneuver.

Von Braun and others float weightlessly inside the KC-135 during a microgravity maneuver.

Von Braun, between two microgravity parabolas, dons an astronaut's spacesuit to enable him to experience microgravity as astronauts would.

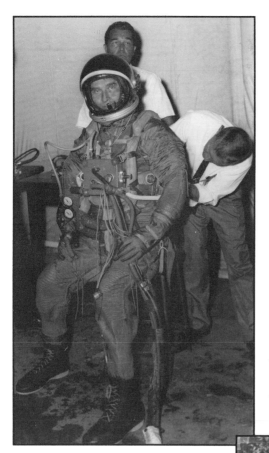

Von Braun, fitted with suit and diving equipment, prepares for a tryout in Marshall's neutral buoyancy tank in mid-November 1967.

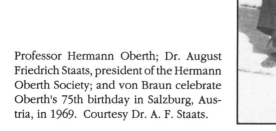

Professor Hermann Oberth; Dr. August Friedrich Staats, president of the Hermann Oberth Society; and von Braun celebrate Oberth's 75th birthday in Salzburg, Austria, in 1969. Courtesy Dr. A. F. Staats.

Meeting for the flight readiness review of the Saturn-Apollo 9 flight, 2 June 1969. Left to right: Dr. George E. Mueller, associate administrator for Manned Space Flight; Air Force Lieutenant General Samuel C. Phillips, Apollo program director; Dr. Kurt H. Debus, director, Kennedy Space Center; Dr. Robert R. Gilruth, director, Manned Spacecraft Center; and von Braun. Courtesy NASA.

Von Braun and Dr. Kurt Debus, director of the Kennedy Space Center, inside the Vertical Assembly Building with a Saturn V in the background, 1969. The VAB was later renamed Vehicle Assembly Building. Courtesy NASA-Kennedy Space Center.

Von Braun stands in front of the Saturn-Apollo 11 launch vehicle/spacecraft combination at the Kennedy Space Center, Florida, before its history-making 16 July 1969 flight to the Moon. Courtesy NASA-Kennedy Space Center.

Successful launch! Saturn-Apollo 11 heads for the Moon on 16 July 1969. Left to right: Charles W. Matthews, NASA deputy associate administrator for Manned Space Flight; von Braun; George E. Mueller, NASA associate administrator for Manned Space Flight; and Air Force Lieutenant General Samuel C. Phillips, Apollo program director. Courtesy NASA-Kennedy Space Center.

Von Braun and Charles A. Lindbergh at the Kennedy Space Center in Florida during the Saturn-Apollo 11 launch on 16 July 1969.

Von Braun in the Launch Control Center, Kennedy Space Center, Florida, during the Apollo 11 mission.

On 24 July 1969, von Braun is carried on the shoulders of enthusiastic Huntsvillians following the successful Apollo 11 flight to the Moon.

Von Braun and Ordway in the former's office of the NASA-Marshall Space Flight Center discussing the second edition (1969) of their book *History of Rocketry & Space Travel* and plans for the post-Apollo exploration of the Moon and Mars.

Wernher and Maria von Braun at the 1969 annual picnic of NASA-Marshall employees, Huntsville, Alabama.

In 1970 NASA Administrator Dr. Thomas O. Paine called for a symposium on future space projects that was subsequently organized by the Langley Research Center and held at the Wallops Island Station on the Atlantic coast of Virginia. Left to right, front row: Edward Schmidt, Dale D. Myers, Jerry Truszinsky, D. D. Wyatt, George M. Low, von Braun, Paine, John E. Naugle, Oran W. Nicks, Arthur C. Clarke, Willis Shapley, Homer E. Newell, and Clare Farley; and, left to right, back row: Neil Armstrong, Robert L. Krieger, Robert Jastrow, Bruce Lundin, Charles W. Matthews, Robert R. Gilruth, Abraham Spinak, Jay N. Foster, Ray Kline, William H. Pickering, and Julian W. Scheer. Courtesy NASA.

Edward O. Buckbee, director of the Alabama (later, U.S.) Space & Rocket Center (left) with von Braun shortly after its opening in 1970. Courtesy U.S. Space & Rocket Center.

Wernher von Braun photographed in 1970. Courtesy Dorette Schlidt.

Top right: Von Braun presents the Gulf Stream Mission Medallion to Chester B. May in August 1969 for his participation in Dr. Auguste Piccard's submarine project to chart the Gulf Stream along the American coast.

Top left: Von Braun and his deputy Eberhard Rees converse during the 1969 annual picnic of Marshall employees.

Middle: Von Braun, Stuhlinger, Barnard, unidentified, and Rees during Barnard's visit at Marshall, February 1970.

Lower right: Dr. Christiaan N. Barnard, heart surgeon from Cape Town, South Africa, chats with (left to right) Stuhlinger, von Braun, and Eberhard Rees at the NASA-Marshall Space Flight Center, 20 February 1970. Courtesy NASA-Marshall Space Flight Center.

Von Braun sports a beard following his return from vacationing in
the Bahamas in February 1970.
Courtesy Mitchell R. Sharpe.

Von Braun appears to enjoy his beard; but,
faced with disapproval from his daughters,
soon had it removed.

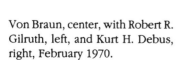

Von Braun, center, with Robert R.
Gilruth, left, and Kurt H. Debus,
right, February 1970.

In early 1970, von Braun was named honorary president of the Von Braun Astronomical Society, which had just been renamed from the former Rocket City Astronomical Association. Left to right: Ernst Stuhlinger, Benjamin Teeter, Wilhelm Angele, Dolores Killion, Wernher von Braun, Milton Cummings, James Donnini, Clarence Ellis, and Donald Parker.

Von Braun embraces Hazel Toftoy, widow of Major General Holger N. Toftoy during ceremonies in downtown Huntsville on 24 February 1970. The occasion: Von Braun's approaching departure for Washington to head up advanced planning at NASA headquarters. Maria von Braun sits at right while Major General Ivey D. Drewry stands behind the podium. Harry Rhett sits behind Maria, to her right. Courtesy NASA-Marshall Space Flight Center.

Wernher and Maria von Braun, center, participate in festivities at Redstone Arsenal on the occasion of their transfer to Washington in March 1970.

VI

Washington, D.C.: The Final Years

1970-1977

Dr. George M. Low, acting NASA administrator, and von Braun observe Apollo 14 prelaunch activities in the Launch Control Center's Firing Room 2, Kennedy Space Center, Florida, 31 January 1971. Courtesy NASA-Kennedy Space Center.

NASA Administrator Dr. James C. Fletcher with von Braun at Cape Canaveral during prelaunch preparations for Apollo 15, 26 July 1971. Courtesy NASA-Kennedy Space Center.

Von Braun describes the operations of the space shuttle in his position as head of future planning at NASA Headquarters, 1971. Courtesy NASA.

NASA Administrator Dr. James C. Fletcher, right, speaks with (left to right) William Anders, executive secretary of the National Aeronautics and Space Council; Lieutenant General Sam Phillips, former Apollo program director; and von Braun, at this point in his career the deputy associate administrator for Future Planning at NASA headquarters in Washington, D.C., during Apollo 15 prelaunch activities at the Launch Control Center's Firing Room 1, Cape Canaveral, Florida, 26 July 1971.

Von Braun standing in front of his sailplane, a glass-fiber "Libelle," 1971. Courtesy Maria von Braun.

Celebration of von Braun's 60th birthday in March 1972 at the home of Dr. and Mrs. Carsbie C. Adams, McLean, Virginia. Left to right: Ahuva Adams, Eberhard Rees, Ernst Stuhlinger, Wernher von Braun, Irmgard Stuhlinger, Maria von Braun, Gerlinde Rees, Edward G. Uhl, and Adams. Courtesy Dr. Carsbie C. Adams.

Three directors of NASA's George C. Marshall Space Flight Center photographed together in 1973: Von Braun (past, right), Dr. Eberhard Rees (present, center), and Dr. Rocco A. Petrone (future, left). Courtesy NASA.

Edward G. Uhl, chairman of the board of Fairchild Industries, Germantown, Maryland, and von Braun. At this point in his career — 1973 — von Braun was vice president, Engineering and Development at the company. Courtesy J. B. Minnich, Fairchild Industries.

Von Braun, singer and space enthusiast John Denver, and radio and television personality Hugh Downs, left to right, discussing plans at a National Space Institute gathering in Washington, D.C., 1974. Courtesy J. B. Minnich, Fairchild Industries.

In his capacity as National Space Institute president, von Braun addresses NSI members in Washington, D.C., in 1974. At right is NSI executive director Charles C. Hewitt. Courtesy J. B. Minnich, Fairchild Industries.

Von Braun stands beside a model of the Saturn V launch vehicle. This photo, taken in 1974, was used frequently by the National Space Institute in response to requests by members for von Braun's photo and autograph. Courtesy National Space Society, successor to NSI.

While visiting the Kennedy Space Center in 1975, von Braun asked, "Will you take my picture in front of Saturn V? I may not be here again." This was the last photo of him with the giant rocket. Courtesy NASA-Kennedy Space Center.

Irvin Singer, chief scientist and vice president for Business Development at Fairchild, left, and von Braun, right, on the occasion of former's 25 years with the company, December 1975. Courtesy Irvin Singer.

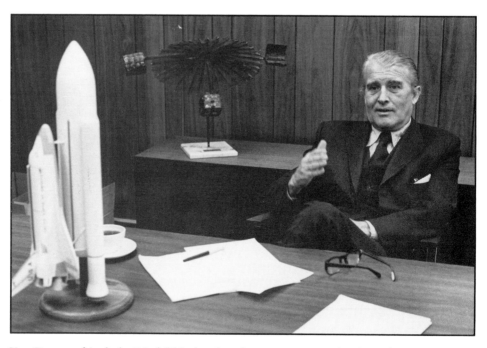

Von Braun at his desk, Fairchild Industries, Germantown, Maryland, 1976. Courtesy J. B. Minnich, Fairchild Industries.

Von Braun and his colleagues discuss the plans and aspirations of the National Space Institute with Vice President Nelson Rockefeller at the White House, Washington, D.C., 21 April 1976. Clockwise from Rockefeller, left foreground back to camera: Charles C. Hewitt, NSI executive director; Jason Stern, Paddock Publications and NSI trustee; Hugh Downs, NSI president; and von Braun, NSI chairman of the board. Courtesy Charles C. Hewitt.

Reunion of members of the von Braun team at the Redstone Arsenal Officers' Club, Huntsville, Alabama on 15 March 1990, close to von Braun's 78th birthday. They were joined there by Marshall Space Flight Center Director Jack Lee and several associates. Left to right: (seated) Elbert Rudder, Hans Milde, Helmut Krause, Werner Rosinski, Heinrich Rothe, Max Nowak, Hans Palaoro, Willibald Prasthofer, William Schulze, Helmut Horn, Gerhard Reisig. Left to right: (middle row) Henning Krome, Axel Roth, Walt Wiesman, Willi Kuberg, Jack Lee, Karl Reilmann, Friedrich Duerr, R. M. Barraza, Ernst Lange, Werner Dahm, Walter Haeussermann, Ernest Nathan, Werner Sieber, Herbert Bergeler, Gerhard Drawe, Hubert Kroh, Karl Heimburg. Left to right: (last row) Hans Kennel, Dieter Grau, Ernst Stuhlinger, Heinrich Hahn, Rudolf Hermann, Ernst Evers-Euterneck, Erich Engler, Heinz Hilten, Grover Daussman, Mario Rheinfurth, Werner Voss, Hans Fichtner, Heinz Kampmeier, Wilhelm Angele, Hans Hosenthien, Ruth von Saurma, and Heinz Struck.

Von Braun in the foyer of the Smithsonian Institution's National Air and Space Museum on 15 March 1976. There, he marked the occasion of the 50th anniversary of the flight of Robert H. Goddard's first liquid propellant-powered rocket in Auburn, Massachusetts. Courtesy Smithsonian Institution-National Air and Space Museum.

VII

Workplaces, Hardware, and Dreams

KUMMERSDORF
Modest Beginnings

Office building at Kummersdorf as it appeared in the mid-1930s.

Kummersdorf test stand with tanks for liquid oxygen and alcohol at right, mid-1930s.

Test Stand No. 2 at Kummersdorf, 1935.

December 1932 test at Kummersdorf of a 300-kilogram thrust motor for the A-2 rocket. Two A-2s were fired from the North Sea island of Borkum in late 1934.

An A-3 on Test Stand 4 at Kummersdorf in 1936; it developed 1,500 kilograms of thrust.

Three attempts to fire A-3s from Greifswalder Oie island in 1937 failed due not to propulsion but to guidance problems.

PEENEMÜNDE
The Flowering of a New Technology

Peenemünde's *Werk Ost* or East Works development fabrication laboratory as viewed towards end of construction in 1937.

Haus 4 at Peenemünde. The window just above the black mark slightly to left of center marks von Braun's office. This photograph was taken in 1943.

Typical worker's housing project at Peenemünde, constructed during 1937 and 1938 and destroyed by RAF bombers in August 1943.

Preproduction assembly of A-4 tanks at Peenemünde, early 1943.

Preproduction assembly of A-4 rocket motors at Peenemünde, early 1943.

Peenemünde underwent a heavy night raid by the RAF in August 1943 and the following year was visited three times by U.S. Army Air Corps bombers. Note the several A-4 rocket motor combustion chambers amidst the rubble in the assembly shop.

Damaged service towers in Peenemünde's test area. These towers serviced complete A-4 rockets and also were used to support static-test operations, as well as cold-flow and pump check-out.

A rocket-powered Me-163 takes off at Peenemünde in August 1941.

After the A-3 disappointment, the A-5 — forerunner of the much larger A-4 — was developed. Between 1937 and 1939, about 25 were fired. The experimental rocket had a complete gyroscopic guidance system, jet vane controls, and radio guide beam.

German Army troops service an A-4 in the field, which by the time it entered combat in September 1944, was known as the V-2 vengeance weapon.

An A-4 undergoes simulated winter combat-launch servicing in 1943.

A Schmetterling surface-to-air missile undergoes a test firing at Peenemünde.

The liquid-propellant rocket-powered Wasserfall sur-face-to-air missile at the moment of takeoff at Peenemünde. The first fully successful guided flight of the missile occurred in February 1944.

By adding wings to the A-4, the A-4b (b for bastard) was developed and flown twice in January 1944. The idea was to extend the A-4's range from roughly 200 to over 400 miles. If development had continued, the A-4b would have become known as the A-9.

By combining three conceptual stages desig-nated A-11, A-10, and the A-4b-derived A-9, a three-stage launch vehicle capable of orbiting satellites would have evolved. The war ended before this ambitious project could be pursued.

FORT BLISS - WHITE SANDS
Transition Period

Rooftop view of Fort Bliss, Texas, where the Germans worked for nearly five years following their arrival from Europe.

White Sands Proving Ground, New Mexico, as it appeared when the Germans arrived to convert V-2s to upper atmosphere sounding rockets. Courtesy Mitchell R. Sharpe.

Test stand at White Sands capable of accommodating rocket engines producing up to 500,000 pounds of thrust.

A V-2 being serviced at White Sands, New Mexico.

An instrumented V-2 takes off from White Sands to probe the upper atmosphere. The first such launch in April 1946 was a failure but the second, in May, reached an altitude of just over 70 miles.

By adding an American-made Wac-Corporal rocket as a second stage, the V-2 was able to boost a payload up to 244 miles in Febuary 1949 within the so-called "Bumper" series of flights. Six Bumpers were launched from White Sands, two from Cape Canaveral, Florida.

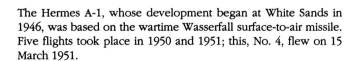

The Hermes A-1, whose development began at White Sands in 1946, was based on the wartime Wasserfall surface-to-air missile. Five flights took place in 1950 and 1951; this, No. 4, flew on 15 March 1951.

REDSTONE ARSENAL
Army Period

Redstone Arsenal headquarters as it appeared in the early 1950s when the von Braun team was commencing a new phase of rocket development.

Test firing at Redstone Arsenal of the Saturn I's 1,300,000-pound-thrust first stage.

Top left: The Redstone surface-to-surface missile evolved from V-2 experience and remained in service with the U.S. Army for many years. First test-fired in 1953, it entered operational service in Germany in 1958. Here, missile #1002 rests on its launch pad at Cape Canaveral, 16 May 1958.

Top center: The Jupiter intermediate-range ballistic missile followed the Redstone in the development cycle. Seen here at the moment of a nighttime launch at Cape Canaveral, it first flew in March 1957 and was subsequently deployed in both Italy and Turkey.

Top right: First firing in February 1960 of the Pershing solid-propellant ballistic missile. With a range of some 450 miles, it was designed to replace the liquid-propellant Redstone in the field.

Bottom left: The Jupiter-C reentry test vehicle consisted of a Redstone first stage and two upper solid-propellant stages. Here, round 27 is being serviced prior to its record-breaking flight on 20 September 1956 when it attained the then astonishing altitude of nearly 700 miles and range of 3,400 miles from Cape Canaveral. Courtesy U.S. Army.

Bottom right: Juno I was a Jupiter-C rocket to which a fourth solid-propellant stage and satellite payload were added. On 31 January 1958, a Juno I orbited Explorer 1, America's first artificial Earth satellite. Courtesy U.S. Army.

When outfitted with Juno I upper stages, the Jupiter IRBM became known as Juno II. On 3 March 1959, this Juno II sent the Pioneer 4 lunar fly-by probe to within 37,000 miles of the Moon.

The 13.4-pound Pioneer 4 spacecraft. Courtesy NASA.

America's first man in space, astronaut Navy Lieutenant Commander Alan B. Shepard, was lofted in his "Freedom" capsule by this Redstone-Mercury I rocket on 5 May 1961. Courtesy NASA.

Shepard's Mercury "Freedom" capsule is retrieved following its historic voyage. Courtesy NASA.

THE REALIZATION OF A DREAM
Saturn -Apollo Years

View of the NASA-Marshall Space Flight Center, located at Redstone Arsenal, Huntsville, Alabama. The headquarters building, familiarly known as the "Von Braun Hilton," is seen behind the shuttle "Enterprise" in March 1978, the year following von Braun's death. Courtesy NASA-Marshall.

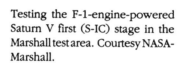

The NASA-Marshall test area. Courtesy NASA-Marshall.

Testing the F-1-engine-powered Saturn V first (S-IC) stage in the Marshall test area. Courtesy NASA-Marshall.

In this spectacular night launch, Saturn I flight SA-8 lifts off Pad 37 at Cape Canaveral with a Pegasus micrometeoroid-measuring satellite aboard. Courtesy NASA-Kennedy.

Inset: Mating of the Pegasus satellite with the SA-8 launch vehicle. Courtesy NASA-Kennedy.

A Saturn IB lifts off from Launch Complex 34 at Cape Canaveral on 11 October 1968 carrying the Apollo 7 three-man spacecraft into Earth orbit. This first manned Apollo test flight was commanded by Navy Captain Walter M. Schirra, Jr., accompanied by Major Donn F. Eisele of the Air Force and Walter Cunningham, a civilian physicist. Courtesy NASA-Kennedy.

Established by the Marshall Center in October 1961 to test large Saturn-class rockets, this facility was first known as Mississippi Test Operations and shortly afterwards as the Mississippi Test Facility. Then, in July 1974, its name changed to the National Space Technology Laboratories and at the same time was reassigned from Marshall to NASA Headquarters for reporting purposes. Finally, in May 1988, the complex became the John C. Stennis Space Center. This photo was taken of the Saturn V test site at the Mississippi Test Facility in 1968. Courtesy NASA-John C. Stennis Space Center.

Saturn launch vehicles were assembled here at the Michaud Assembly Facility near New Orleans, Louisiana.

Apollo 11 is shown mounted on its Saturn V carrier at Launch Complex 39-A, Cape Canaveral, Florida. The spacecraft departed for the Moon on 16 July 1969 with astronauts Neil A. Armstrong, Air Force Colonel Edwin E. ("Buzz") Aldrin, Jr., and Air Force Lieutenant Colonel Michael Collins aboard. The three pioneering space voyagers reached the moon on the 20th. Courtesy NASA.

Inset: Apollo 11's Lunar Module rests on the Moon as Astronaut Aldrin prepares to perform scientific experiments. Courtesy NASA.

Astronaut James B. Irwin stands by the Lunar Rover during Apollo 15's mission to the Hadley-Appenine site, 30 July 1971. The use of the Rover greatly extended the radius of exploration during this and the following two (and last) Apollo missions. Courtesy NASA.

Overhead view of the Skylab space station photographed from the Apollo command and service-module combination placed into orbit by a Saturn IB rocket. Earlier, in mid-May 1973, the space station itself had been orbited by a Saturn V. Skylab was visited by three crews over successive 28-, 59-, and 84-day periods during 1973 and 1974. Courtesy NASA-Marshall.

The final payload launched by a Saturn-series rocket was an Apollo command and service module combination specially modified to enable it to dock with a Soviet Soyuz spacecraft within the Apollo Soyuz Test Project. On 15 July 1975, Soyuz 19 was launched from the Baikonur Cosmodrome and 7½ hours later a Saturn IB lofted the Apollo CSM into orbit with Thomas P. Stafford, Vance D. Brand, and Donald K. Slayton aboard. They docked on the 17th with the Soviet spacecraft manned by veteran cosmonauts Aleksei A. Leonov and Valery N. Kubasov. Over the next two days, four crew transfers were made before the two craft disengaged. This view of the approaching Soyuz was photographed from Apollo's rendezvous window. Courtesy NASA.

Inset: Artist's concept of the Apollo CSM, docking adapter, and Soyuz when mated in space. Courtesy NASA-Marshall Space Flight Center.

PROMOTING THE FUTURE
THROUGH THE PAGES OF *COLLIER'S*
1952-1954

By the beginning of the 1950s, the general public had only the vaguest notion of America's nascent rocket program and evolving ideas of space travel. The United States was engaged in a cold war with the Soviet Union and a hot war in Korea; it was a period that found rocket development and occasional studies of space travel almost exclusively controlled by the military and for the most part subjected to security classification.

At the same time, the stage was being set for the publication of a series of mass-circulation magazine articles depicting the wonders and promise of space travel. Through them the public would learn what might be accomplished in the not too distant future.

The first event leading to these articles occurred on the 12th of October 1951, when the Hayden Planetarium in New York City hosted the first of three symposia on space travel. The speakers were acknowledged leaders in rocketry and missile development, astronomy, biological and medical aspects of flight into space, and related fields. In the audience were scientists, engineers, military officers, and — perhaps most important — members of the press. As the symposium proceedings were not to be published, it was largely through the press that the public became aware of what had transpired at Hayden.

Several weeks later, *Collier's* magazine — having been inspired by staff attendance at the symposium — sent associate editor Cornelius Ryan to a conference in San Antonio, Texas, on the physics and medicine of the upper atmosphere. There, rocket expert Wernher von Braun, astronomer Fred L. Whipple, and physicist Joseph Kaplan convinced him not only that man would one day travel into space but that it could happen in the relatively near future. Ryan, in turn, suggested to his superiors at *Collier's* the idea of bringing together von Braun, Whipple, Kaplan, and other experts for a symposium at the magazine's New York editorial offices. The idea, subsequently put into practice, was to publish the findings of the symposium as a special series of articles in *Collier's*. Such an approach would bring the excitement of spaceflight into the homes of millions of readers.

During 1952, 1953, and 1954, *Collier's* delivered, with Ryan and his magazine colleagues enlisting not only the services of the experts but three of the nation's outstanding artists, Chesley Bonestell, Fred Freeman, and Rolf Klep. It was their collaboration with scientists and engineers that brought spaceflight a little closer to reality.

CAPTIONS FOR COLOR SECTION
Reference with Plate No.

PLATE 1
To loft passengers and cargo into orbit, von Braun designed a three-stage launch vehicle whose third stage we see separating from the second stage in this rendering by Chesley Bonestell. The spent second stage, whose outer engines can be swiveled for steering, is dropping back from the just-ignited winged third stage. This stage contains 36 tons of cargo being sent to an orbit 1,075 miles high — the 2-hour orbit in which von Braun planned to establish his ring-shaped manned space station.

PLATE 2
Men and materials arrive in the recoverable third stage. Small space "taxis" are then employed to travel to and from the astronomical observatory (upper center left), the 250-foot diameter, wheel-shaped space station (right), or any other nearby orbiting craft.

PLATE 3
Von Braun described his space station, seen in this Fred Freeman cutaway, as "A self-contained community [that would] provide all of man's needs, from air conditioning to artificial gravity."

PLATE 4
In this retro-propulsion maneuver illustrated by Bonestell, the winged stage's velocity is reduced causing the craft to swing back towards Earth.

Years after the space station had been in operation, von Braun believed, the next logical step in man's conquest of space should be the exploration of the Moon. The components needed to construct three lunar landing craft were to be ferried up into Earth orbit and assembled there for the journey to the lunar surface.

PLATE 5
Two winged third stages unload supplies in orbit in this Bonestell painting. Above them is the space station and below the lunar-bound cargo ship. In the center and right foreground are the two passenger ships being assembled by space-suited workers.

PLATE 6
Cutaway view executed by Freeman of one of two passenger vehicles planned for expeditions capable of accommodating 20 men

en route to the Moon and 25 on the return trip to Earth (10 men on the one-way cargo ship will split up coming back).

PLATE 7

Hypothetical lunar landscape as it might be seen by a visitor standing on the inner slope of a crater wall and looking across the 30-mile wide floor. The observer's position is about 1,300 feet above the floor of a crater located 7 degrees from the Moon's north pole and 5 degrees to the left of the center line of the lunar disk. Since there is no appreciable atmosphere, Bonestell painted the sky jet black and filled with unblinking stars. Some distant, tall mountains are glaringly brilliant in direct sunlight, while other peaks and the crater floor are bathed in bluish light from the Earth, some 60 times stronger than the light we experience from the full Moon. To the right, we see the Earth, apparently suspended among the stars of Ophiuchus. Jupiter is the bright planet over the central peaks, while Mars is near the 16,000-foot peak to the left. The ecliptic passes approximately through these and the Earth. It is June-July on our planet, as its north pole is tipped about 23 degrees toward the Sun. The reflection of the Sun is on the Lower California peninsula of North America. Parts of the Milky Way are seen as hazy patches of light.

PLATE 8

Three spacecraft descend 500 miles above the lunar surface, their rocket motors having just been ignited to reduce the high velocity acquired during the long fall moonward. The intended landing area in this Bonestell panorama is the plain to the left of center in the picture, partly obscured by the exhaust blast of the cargo ship (lower left). The single crater just above the center is *Harpalus*, the large "bay" to its right is *Sinus Iridum*, and the large crater near the upper right-hand corner is *Plato*.

PLATE 9

In this faithful copy by space artist Ron Miller of the Bonestell original whose location is unknown, acrylics rather than oils were used; otherwise, he followed the same techniques Bonestell employed (for example, his methods for creating textures). Miller allowed for the poorer color reproduction processes of the 1950s by using slightly more saturated colors.

A historic moment: man's first landing on the Moon. The rocket motors are being turned off as the shock-absorbing central landing leg (visible inside the flames) is just about to touch the lunar surface. This view, with the Earth in the background, was painted by Bonestell from the perspective of a man standing on the lunar north pole.

PLATE 10

About 24 hours after arrival at *Sinus Roris,* the three spaceships have been stripped of their landing propellant tanks, and movable equipment has been stored on caterpillar tractors and trailers in this Bonestell rendering. In the foreground the cargo hold is being lowered in sections to make the prefabricated lunar base.

PLATE 11

Here, Bonestell depicts a convoy of tractors, each pulling two trailers, that travels slowly across rough lunar terrain near the plain of *Sinus Roris* (Bay of Dew). Glare of mountain range to north is caused by the setting Sun; the rest of the scene is illuminated by greenish light from planet Earth. Ten men are making the trip with enough fuel and supplies to last about a fortnight. Average land speed: 2 miles an hour.

PLATE 12

This underground base, executed by Freeman, protects the lunar explorers from meteorites and cosmic rays during their 6-week stay. The cylindrical hold of the cargo-carrying space vehicle has already been split into lengthwise halves, 75 feet long and 36 feet wide, and lowered by sections into the chasm by cranes mounted on lunar tractors. One of the halves serves as the laboratory and the other as the habitat module.

Some decades after man's arrival on the Moon and the establishment of bases there, von Braun prophesied Mars would become the target of exploration. His plan required a flotilla of 10 ships that would assemble in Earth orbit prior to embarking on the multi-million-mile interplanetary adventure.

Before landing on Mars, one of its two moons would likely be visited. The next step would be to land a single ship on one of the Martian poles, chosen because of the flat terrain expected there. After disembarking, the crew would travel towards the equator on tractors that also serve as mobile living quarters. Once the equator was reached, a landing strip would be prepared to receive two other landing ships that had been waiting in orbit.

With the full complement of Martian explorers now on the surface, a 15-month-long period of study would begin. When it had been completed, preparations would be made for the explorers to ascend from the surface to orbit. Once there, preparations could be made to depart on the long journey back to Earth.

PLATE 13
In 1954, Wernher von Braun, Chesley Bonestell, and Fred Freeman turned their attention to Mars calling on extrapolations of the vehicular technology developed for their lunar voyage. In this Bonestell painting, we recognize the large, wheel-shaped space station in the background and the familiar assemblage of deep space vehicles. However, instead of two lunar passenger ships plus the single cargo vessel, the Mars expedition called for 10 spaceships to make the 355 million-mile, 8-month trip. The round trip, including a stay-time on the red planet of 15 months, was estimated to take more than 2½ years.

PLATE 14
In 1954, Wernher von Braun felt it was possible to "discuss the problems of a flight to Mars in terms of what is known today. We can assume," he wrote, "that such an expedition will involve about 70 scientists and crew members. A force that size would require a flotilla of 10 massive space ships, each weighing more than 4,000 tons — not only because there's safety in numbers, but because of the tons of fuel, scientific equipment, rations, oxygen, water and the like necessary for the trip and for a stay of about 31 months away from earth." In this Ron Miller reproduction of the lost Bonestell original, we see the flotilla approaching the red planet.

PLATE 15
Von Braun envisaged the situation a century or so from the time he wrote when a fleet of spaceships might set off for Mars, three of which are depicted in this Fred Freeman painting. "The trip could be made with 10 ships launched from an orbit, about 1,000 miles out in space," von Braun proposed. "The Mars-bound vehicles, assembled in the orbit, will look like bulky bundles of girders, with propellant tanks hung on the outside and great passenger cabins perched on top. Three of them will have torpedo-shaped noses and massive wings — dismantled, but strapped to their sides for future use. Those bullet noses will be detached and will serve as landing craft, the only vehicles that will actually land on the neighbor planet. When the 10 ships are 5,700 miles from the earth, they will cut off their rocket motors; from there on, they will coast unpowered toward Mars.

"After eight months," von Braun continued, "they will swing into an orbit around Mars, about 600 miles up . . . The expedition will take this intermediate step, instead of proceeding directly to Mars, for two main reasons: first, the ships (except for the three detachable torpedo-shaped noses) will lack the streamlining required for flight in the Martian atmosphere; second, it will be more economical to avoid carrying all the fuel needed for the return to earth (which now comprises the bulk of the cargo) all the way down to Mars and then back up again."

PLATE 16
"Upon reaching the 600-mile orbit — and after some exploratory probings of Mars' atmosphere with unmanned rockets — the first of the three landing craft will be assembled," explained von Braun. "The torpedo nose will be unhooked, to become the fuselage of a rocket plane. The wings and a set of landing skis will be attached, and the plane launched toward the surface of Mars." Here Bonestell has illustrated the maneuvers taking place in Martian orbit.

Von Braun felt that the first plane should land on a polar cap because it would be the only place reasonably certain to be flat. Once there, he explained, the "pioneer landing party will unload its tractors and supplies, inflate its balloonlike living quarters, and start (in a tractor train) on a 4,000-mile overland journey to the Martian equator, where the expedition's main base will be set up . . . At the equator, the advance party will construct a landing strip for the other two rocket planes . . ." (These in the meantime will have remained in orbit above; the first craft, incidentally, will have been abandoned at the pole.)

At the end of 15 months, the two rockets would have their wings stripped off, would be set on their tails, and then would be sent back to rendezvous and dock with the awaiting fleet of seven space vehicles in orbit above. Unfortunately, winged landing schemes such as this no longer appear feasible because the Martian atmosphere has been found to be extremely thin. The Viking 1 spacecraft regularly measured the Chryse Basin atmospheric pressure at between 7 and 8 millibars, less than 1 percent of Earth's atmospheric pressure at sea level. Decades earlier, when von Braun was composing his text, astronomers assumed Martian ground-level pressure to be a twelfth that of Earth's sea level pressure or about 8 percent.

PLATE 17
Fred Freeman painted this scene of the advance landing party on the snowy surface of Mars following its arrival in the ski-equipped plane. Men prepare to travel towards the equator in these inflatable, pressurized spheres mounted on tractors; they enter and leave through air locks in the central column. The sphere on the tractor at

rear center is in the process of being inflated. The cutaway of the foreground tractor shows the closed-circuit engine, which is run by hydrogen peroxide and oil. The trailer cutaway reveals the fuel supply and cargo.

PLATE 18

Wrote von Braun in 1954: "When, at last, Mars and the earth begin to come closer together on their elliptic orbits around the Sun, and it's time to go back, the two ships that landed on the equator will be stripped of their wings and landing gear, set on their tails and, at the proper moment, rocketed back to the 600-mile orbit on the first leg of the return journey." In this Ron Miller rendition of a Bonestell original whose location is unknown, one vehicle is already in the upright position and its companion in the left background is in the process of being raised.

DREAMS UNFULFILLED

PLATES 19, 20, 21

Von Braun's unfulfilled dream was the manned exploration of Mars, a subject he had studied intensively beginning in the late 1940s. From the vantage point of the Apollo era, he and at least some of his associates at the NASA-Marshall Center would have liked nothing more than follow the Apollo program with a manned mission to Mars. Eventually, they were convinced, early Moon and Mars exploration missions would be followed by large Earth-orbiting space stations; by small outposts first on the Moon and later on Mars; and, in the more distant future, by permanent settlements on those worlds.

However, von Braun was too much a realist to lose himself in futuristic daydreaming. A "scouting mission" to Mars with a small number of astronauts, extending over not more than 1 or 1½ years, would be the utmost that could realistically be planned and expected in the following decades. As the Apollo program neared its climax, plans for such a mission were considered by NASA Associate Administrator George E. Mueller and by NASA Administrator Thomas O. Paine, and eagerly supported by von Braun. He worked out a number of details for the flight plan, particularly for the necessary landing maneuvers, and he showed that a manned Mars mission could be accomplished either with two novel nuclear-powered space rockets or with five or six conventional rockets of the Saturn V type, provided that the president and Congress supported such a program with national resolve and funding.

Despite many carefully thought out and promoted plans for post-Apollo space exploration, before the Apollo lunar expeditions were over in late 1972, it had become clear that priorities in the United States were shifting away from space. Mars would have to wait for some future generation. Courtesy NASA-Marshall.

PLATE 1

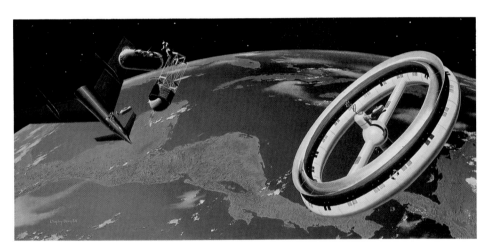

PLATE 2

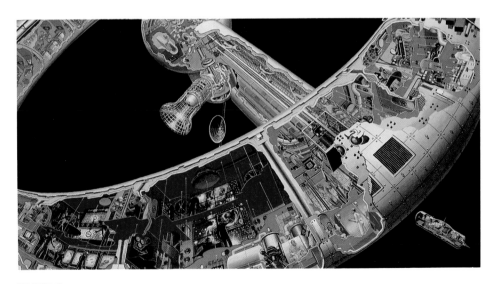

PLATE 3

125

PLATE 4

PLATE 5

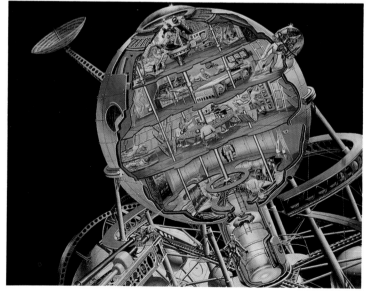

PLATE 6

PLATE 7

PLATE 8

PLATE 9

PLATE 10

PLATE 11

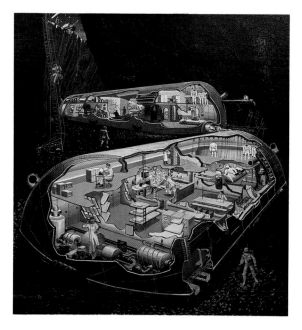

PLATE 12

PLATE 13

PLATE 14

PLATE 15

PLATE 16

PLATE 17

PLATE 18

Dreams Unfulfilled

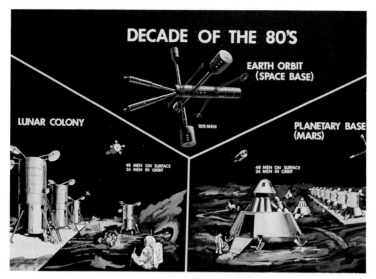

PLATE 19

PLATE 20

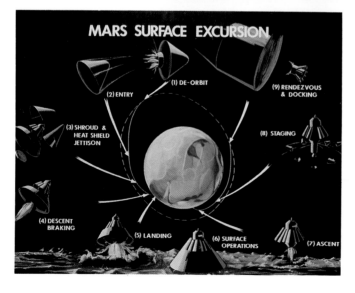

PLATE 21

VIII

In Memoriam

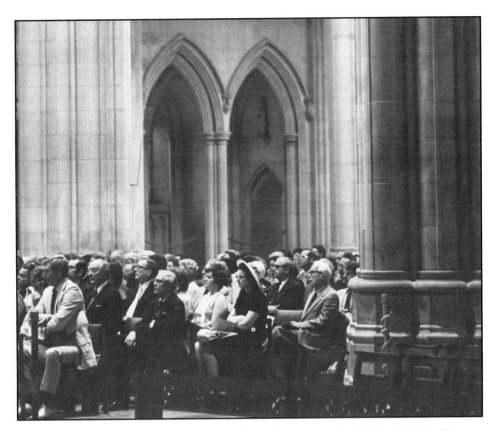

Memorial service for Wernher von Braun at the Washington National Cathedral, Washington, D.C., 22 June 1977. Dean of the Cathedral, the Very Reverend Francis B. Sayre, Jr., officiated and eulogies were presented by NASA Administrator James C. Fletcher, Apollo 11 astronaut and National Air and Space Museum director Michael Collins, and Stuhlinger.

Von Braun was buried in Alexandria, Virginia, on 17 June 1977, the day after his death on the 16th.

Principal Awards and Honors

Accorded Wernher von Braun

1952
Honorary Citizen, Boys Town, Nebraska

1955
Appointment to Committee on Aircraft Construction from the National Advisory Committee for Aeronautics

Designated "Certified Missileer Expert" by the U.S. Air Force Missile Test Center

Astronautics Award by the American Rocket Society

1957
Distinguished Civilian Service Award of the Department of Defense, presented by Secretary of Defense Charles E. Wilson

Degree of Oozlefinching, First Class, Fort Bliss, Texas

Decoration for Exceptional Civilian Service, presented by Secretary of the Army Wilbur E. Brucker

1958
Recipient of the 1957 Space Flight Award by the American Astronautical Society

American Airlines, Commission: Admiral of the Fleet

Diploma de Conselheiro: Life Membership in the Scientific Council, in the Quality of Rocket Engineer, Sao Paulo, Brazil

Outstanding Employee, Department of the Army

Sports Illustrated Award

Dr. Robert H. Goddard Memorial Award

Jupiter Model: U.S. Air Force

Great Living Americans Award of the U.S. Chamber of Commerce

First Honor of the Nationalities Committee Award, People-to-People Program

1959
President's Award for Distinguished Federal Civilian Service, presented by President Dwight D. Eisenhower

Notre Dame Patriotism Award

Charles L. Harrison Award and Medal for Distinguished Ordnance Service

Outstanding Employee, Department of the Army

Honorary Doughboy Award, U.S. Army Infantry School, Fort Benning, Georgia

Operation Hardtack, Participation with Joint Task Force Seven

Replica of Explorer 1 Motor Award, Globe Industries, Dayton, Ohio

Junior Chamber of Commerce Plaque, Canton, Ohio

Southern Association of Science and Industry Plaque

Americanism Award and Medal, presented by the Daughters of the American Revolution

1960
Certificate of Appreciation, Association of the United States Army

Award for Distinguished Service and Outstanding Achievement in Serving the Human Needs of the Community, United Givers Fund

Science Award for Outstanding Scientific Achievement in Man's Conquest of Space, Electronics Institute

Outstanding Employee, Department of the Army

Voted one of Ten Outstanding Young Men of America, U.S. Junior Chamber of Commerce

1961
Award for Outstanding Performance, Department of the Army

Made Honorary Citizen of Decatur, Alabama

Resolution: Invitation to Address the Joint Session of the Arkansas General Assembly

Awarded Gold Panning Rights on the Gold Beach of Nome, Alaska

Made Honorary Citizen of New Orleans, Louisiana

Gold Medal Award presented by the British Interplanetary Society

Hermann Oberth Award by the American Rocket Society (including bust of Professor Oberth)

International Boss of the Year, International Secretaries Association

1962
International Order of Merit, City of New Orleans, Louisiana

Elliot Cresson Medal, Franklin Institute

French Order of Merit for Research and Invention, Paris

1964
Medal for Outstanding Leadership, National Aeronautics and Space Administration

1965
Diesel Medal awarded by the German Society for Promotion of Technology and Invention, Nuremberg

1966
German Society for Aviation and Space Medicine Award, Munich

Named "Engineer of the Century" by an International Press poll conducted by *Hobby* magazine, Stuttgart

Recipient, Wilhelm Bölsche Award, German Kosmos Club

1967
Recipient, Langley Medal of the Smithsonian Institution (one of seven ever awarded)

Court of Honor, Alabama District, Exchange Clubs International

Recipient, Galabert International Astronautical Prize, Paris, France

Named "Man of the Year" by the American Society of Mechanical Engineers

Named "Man of the Year in Science" by the Associated Press

1968
Academy of Honor, State of Alabama

Recipient, Aéro-Club de France award, Paris (for book *L'Histoire mondiale de l'astronautique*)

1969
Honor Award, National Space Hall of Fame

Recipient, German Medal, for First Moon Landing

Awarded Distinguished Service Medal, National Aeronautics and Space Administration (two, one in Houston, one in Huntsville)

Named "Man of the Year" by the Fire Department Steuben Association, Bayside, New York

Named "Man of the Year" by *Industrial Research* Magazine, Chicago

Contribution to the Space Age Award by the Germania Club, Chicago

1970
Recipient, World Citizen Award, International Civitan Club

Awarded Freedom Foundation National Recognition, Valley Forge, Pennsylvania

Founders Award, American Institute of Industrial Engineers

Outstanding Achievement Award, Institute of Electrical and Electronics Engineers

Distinguished Public Service Award, Ohio Newspaper Association

First Founder's Medal, German Society of Pennsylvania, Philadelphia

Made an Honorary Ohioan, plaque presented by Governor James A. Rhoades

Recipient of the Outstanding Achievement Award, Institute of Electrical and Electronics Engineers during Reliability Physics Symposium, Washington, D.C.

AIIE Founder's Award, Cleveland, Ohio

Russian Medal presented by the Cosmonaut Corps

1972
Federal Cross of Merit, Germany

1976
International Space Hall of Fame, Alamogordo, New Mexico

Congressional Resolution of Appreciation, House Committee on Science and Technology

1977
National Medal of Science, presented by President Gerald Ford

1978
(posthumous)
Statuette, Knight of Armor, presented by the Government of Italy

Certificate and Medal: induction into the White Sands Hall of Fame, presented by the Department of the Army for "outstanding service"

1981
Ring, presented by the Association of Former Peenemünders, Germany

Honorary Degrees
Awarded Wernher von Braun

JUNE 1958
Doctor of Science, University of Alabama, Tuscaloosa, Alabama

Doctor of Science, St. Louis University, St. Louis, Missouri

Doctor of Laws, University of Chattanooga, Chattanooga, Tennessee

Doctor of Science, University of Pittsburgh, Pittsburgh, Pennsylvania

FEBRUARY 1959
Doctor of Science, Canisius College, Chester, Pennsylvania

JUNE 1959
Doctor of Laws, Pennsylvania Military College, Chester, Pennsylvania

Doctor of Science, Clark University, Worcester, Massachusetts

Doctor of Laws, Adelphi College, Garden City, New York

JANUARY 1963
Doctor of Engineering, Technische Universität, Berlin, Germany

MARCH 1963
Doctor of Philosophy, Sunshine University, St. Petersburg, Florida

OCTOBER 1963
Doctor of Science, Universidad Nacional de Córdoba, Argentina

NOVEMBER 1963
Doctor of Laws, William Jewell College, Liberty, Missouri

JUNE 1964
Doctor of Science, Iowa Wesleyan College, Mount Pleasant, Iowa

Doctor of Space Science, Brevard Engineering College, Melbourne, Florida (now, Florida Institute of Technology)

MARCH 1965
Doctor of Laws, Iona College, New Rochelle, New York

JUNE 1965
Doctor of Science, Wagner College, Staten Island, New York

Doctor of Science, Emory University, Atlanta, Georgia

NOVEMBER 1965
Doctor of Science, Butler University, Indianapolis, Indiana

JUNE 1966
Doctor of Science, Bradley University, Peoria, Illinois

NOVEMBER 1967
Doctor of Science, D'Youville College, Buffalo, New York

JANUARY 1969
Doctor of Science, University of South Dakota, Vermillion, South Dakota

FEBRUARY 1969
Doctor of Science, Rollins College, Winter Park, Florida

APRIL 1971
Doctor of Laws, Pepperdine College, Los Angeles, California

MAY 1972
Doctor of Humane Letters, Belmont Abbey College, Belmont, North Carolina

APRIL 1974
Doctor of Engineering, Notre Dame University, South Bend, Indiana

Von Braun Memorial Lectures

Delivered at the Smithsonian Institution's National Air and Space Museum
Washington, D.C.

1978
Dr. Ernst Stuhlinger, "Von Braun's Contributions to Rocketry"

1979
Dr. Rocco A. Petrone, "Reflections on von Braun and the Saturn-Apollo Team"

1980
Dr. Edward C. Stone, "Jupiter and Saturn: New Views and Discoveries"

1981
Dr. James A. Van Allen, "The Magnetospheres of the Planets"

1982
John F. Yardley, "Space Shuttle: From Earth to Orbit"

1983
Dr. William H. Pickering, "Explorer 1 Revisited"

1984
Lt. Gen. James A. Abrahamson, USAF-Ret., "The Space Shuttle Revolution"

1985
Christopher C. Kraft, Jr., "Mission Control from Mercury to Shuttle"

1986
Dr. John H. McElroy, "Looking at Earth: From Satellites to Space Stations"

1987
Dr. Thomas O. Paine, "Outward Bound: The Extra-Terrestrial Century"

1988
Gen. Samuel C. Phillips, USAF-Ret., "Destination Space: Managing
the U.S. Space Program"

1989
Dr. John L. McLucas, "Mission to Planet Earth"

1990
Lt. Gen. Bernard A. Schriever, USAF-Ret., "ICBMs to SDI: Space and National
Security"

1991
Ruben F. Mettler, "New Horizons: American Space Policy
in a Changing World"

1992
Norman R. Augustine, "America's Space Program: Wishing Upon a Star
or Going to the Stars?"

1993
Daniel S. Goldin and Dr. Alex Roland, "Colonizing Space: What is our Goal?"

Selected Works

Von Braun, Wernher, *Das Marsprojekt: Studie einer Interplanetarischen Expedition*. Frankfurt am Main, 1952: Unschau; translated as *The Mars Project*, Urbana, 1953, 1962, and 1991: University of Illinois Press (last edition with foreword by Thomas O. Paine).

Von Braun, Wernher et al., edited by Cornelius Ryan, *Across the Space Frontier*. New York, 1952: Viking Press.

Von Braun, Wernher et al., edited by Cornelius Ryan, *Conquest of the Moon*. New York, 1953: Viking Press.

Ley, Willy, and Wernher von Braun, *The Exploration of Mars*. New York, 1956: Viking Press.

Von Braun, Wernher, *First Men to the Moon*. New York, 1960: Holt, Rinehart & Winston.

Adams, Carsbie C., Wernher von Braun, and Frederick I. Ordway III, *Careers in Astronautics and Rocketry*. New York, 1962: McGraw-Hill.

Von Braun, Wernher, and Frederick I. Ordway III, *History of Rocketry & Space Travel*. New York, 1966 (revised and updated in 1969 and 1975): Thos. Y. Crowell; with Dave Dooling, *Space Travel: A History*. New York, 1985: Harper & Row (final revised and updated edition of *History of Rocketry & Space Travel);* and von Braun, Wernher, and Frederick I. Ordway III, *L'Histoire mondiale de l'astronautique*. Paris, 1968: Larousse/ Paris Match (expanded version of 1966 edition of *History of Rocketry & Space Travel)*.

Von Braun, Wernher, *Space Frontier*. New York, 1967: Holt, Rinehart and Winston, reprinted by Fawcett in 1969 (revised and updated Holt edition, 1971).

Von Braun, Wernher, Silvio A. Bedina, and Fred L. Whipple, *Moon: Man's Greatest Adventure*. New York, 1973: Harry N. Abrams.

Von Braun, Wernher, and Frederick I. Ordway III, *The Rockets' Red Glare: An Illustrated History of Rocketry Through the Ages*. New York, 1976: Doubleday/Anchor Press.

Von Braun, Wernher, and Frederick I. Ordway III, *New Worlds: Discoveries from our Solar System*. Garden City, New York, 1979: Doubleday/Anchor Press.

Index